Qi-Gong Life-Nurturing

Qi-Gong Life-Nurturing

Series 3

Wu-Qin-Xi

'Five Animal Frolics'

五禽戲

Yajun Zhuang

Baton Rouge, Louisiana
2019

Life-nurturing is the Tao
Body-exercise is the art
养生是道，养身是术

Nurturing the natural body
by observing the natural law.
----Ou-Yang-Xiu (1107-1073)
Chinese reputable statesman and historian

以自然之道，养自然之身
(宋) 欧阳修

Copyright

Qi-Gong Life-Nurturing/by Zhuang, Yajun

ISBN: 9781657277403

Printed in the United of America

Cover designed by Mr. Chongyang Man
Edited by Ms. Shawei Chen

I dedicated this book to
my family
my friends
my students

Contents

Chapter 3

Forward

Qi-Gong is a traditional Chinese 'Life Nurturing' exercise. The practice of Qi-Gong consists of breathing adjustments and body movements with mind flows regulations. The ultimate goals of Qi-Gong practice are to strengthen the body, prevent diseases, and promote longevity. The practice of Qi-Gong has its ancient originations in China culture. It is an essential part of Chinese traditional medicine. The classic Qi-Gong theories are established collectively based on the theories of Yin-Yang, Wu-Xing (Five elements), Zang-Fu, Meridians, and Jing-Qi-Shen (essence-energy-spirit). The foundations of these concepts are our daily life, productivity, and health-related practices.

Along with baby boomers stepping into advanced ages, there are considerable developments of researches regarding Qi-Gong's life nurturing effects in the fields of physiology and psychology. Qi-Gong practice can benefit mental, cardiovascular, respiratory, nervous, immune, and muscular systems.

At the beginning of this century, Qi-Gong Management Center within the Sports Bureau at the Chinses Central Government has organized Qi-Gong specialists in various areas to create serials of "healthy Qi-Gong" practice routines based on ancient practices. The newly revamped healthy-Qi-Gong practice routines include Five Animal Frolics, Eight Pieces of Brocade, Six Healing Sounds, and Yi-Jin-Jing, and others. There has been extensive clinical research to support Qi-Gong's effects on human health, fitness, and quality of life.

I have the privilege of knowing Mr. Zhuang for more than 15 years since we worked together at Louisiana State University (LSU) on various research projects. Mr. Zhuang has devoted his whole life to Chinese martial arts. He was selected by officials of his province to start professional Chinese martial arts training at age eight. He had organized his martial arts competition team when he was sixteen. He attended Nanjing Normal University and received systematic martial arts theory education at age seventeen. He has been continuously active in teaching, coaching and officiating at national and internal martial art events after graduating from college. Based on his rich practice experience and extensive research, he has authored more than 20 professional books and papers in Tai chi and Qi-Gong related fields.

Mr. Zhuang arrived at Baton Rouge, Louisiana, in 2003. Researchers at LSU and people in the community has benefited from his profound knowledge of Chinese martial arts ever since. We have worked on research projects related to the health benefits of Tai-Chi and Qi-Gong intervention for people with peripheral neuropathy. This project was extended to people with Parkinsonism subsequently. The research had an immediate impact on the surrounding community due to the incredible improvements exhibited by the participants of the intervention programs. Our program was reported extensively by local news media including television stations and newspapers.

Mr. Zhuang has established Zhuang's Tai-Chi & Kung-Fu Academy in Baton Rouge, LA in 2011. He has been working with different populations and continued his studies in Tai-Chi Qi-Gong teaching tailored to different needs with different populations in his academy. He started this series of books eight years ago backed by constant pondering and research, editing it with the goal to help people learning authentic Chinese life nurturing Qi-Gong practice.

Li Li, Ph.D.
Research Professor, Georgia Southern University, Statesboro, Georgia, USA.
Fellow, American College of Sports Medicine
Fellow, National Academy of Kinesiology (USA)

Preface

Evidence from abundant experimental studies has supported that the world-famous 'Qi-Gong Life Nurturing' is a kind of fitness method and complementary therapy for disease prevention and healing. 'Qi-Gong Life Nurturing', especially 'Health Qi-Gong' has gradually become worldwide health care and rehabilitation exercise and been favored by many domestic and foreign Qi-Gong enthusiasts.

From the emperor, the nobles to the common people, human beings never stop the pursuit of health and longevity. In China, along with the advancement of the scientific civilization during the Spring-Autumn and the Warring States Period (770 B.C-221 B.C), great achievements happened in the culture field with 'various schools of thought rising in swarms and contending with each other'. The thought and method of 'Life Nurturing' became more and more mature in this period. In Shang and Zhou Dynasties (About 160 B.C-221 B.C), the concept of 'longevity and immortality' had been further developed, which led to the development of 'Dao-Yin' with the ultimate goal to obtain eternal longevity and immortality. In many philosophical schools, especially under the influence of 'Tao' theorists, the unity of body and spirit, as well as the thought of the 'Life Nurturing' of motion and cultivation in tranquil have been gradually formed. This has played a great role in promoting the development of 'Life Nurturing' in the future. For example, Lao-Zi advocated that 'man recover the pure and return to nature' and 'cherish no worries and keep away from fame and gain'; Zhuang-Zi thought that 'breathing deeply to get rid of the stale and take in the fresh, imitating a bear climbing and a bird flying all promise longevity'; Confucius held that 'dynamic and static should be in perfect order, and happiness and sadness should be appropriate';

and in 'Lv's Spring – Autumn', it was believed that Essence, Qi and Spirit are the essential substances of life. All these together with the theories of 'Yin-Yang', 'Five Elements' and the concept of relevant adaptation of man to nature held by the confusion have lightened the relationship between natural environment and man's health, produced considerable influence upon the formation of the theories of 'Life Nurturing'. The theory and practice of all these saints unveiled a brand-new stage in the history of ancient Chinese health.

In ancient China, this combination of dynamic and static motion exercise was called 'Dao-Yin.' It uses the mind to guide the Qi to make the breath harmonious and lead the body to be flexible. In essence, it is the combination of breathing and body movement, the combination of static and dynamic conditions, and the combination of internal and external environments. These multiple level combinations to make a life nurturing Qi-Gong is successful. Ancient Chinese created, compiled and recorded many 'Dao Yin' methods for Life Nurturing, such as 'Five Animal Frolics' by famous Chinese physician Hua Tuo in Eastern Han dynasty; 'the inner chapter of Bao-Puzi' by Ge-Hong in Jin Dynasty; and the 'The Origin of Various Diseases' by Dr. Chao Yuanfang in Sui Dynasty; 'Health and Longevity record' by Tao Hongjing in Liang Dynasty; 'Ba-Duan-Jin' in Song Dynasty and 'Yi-Jin-Jing' in Ming Dynasty. Nowadays there are lists of popular fitness exercises, including Tai-Chi Chuan, Qi-Gong, Massage, Wu-Qin-Xi (five animal Frolics), Yi-Jin-Jing (the Classic of changing muscle and tendon), Ba-Duan-Jin (eight pieces of brocades).

'Life nurturing' experts in the past followed the law of nature as the primary criterion and created a variety of 'Moving Qi' and 'Leading Body' Qi-Gong Life Nurturing exercises. They believed that 'life is in me, not in heaven,' which means it is ourselves who control our lives, not the universe. People who ignore this guideline will destroy life. Applying it in the right way will prolong life. In life nurturing, spirit depends on form, and form depends on Qi. The more Qi is stored, the more vigorous life is; without Qi, life is unable to survive. The interdependence of Qi, form, and spirit depends on the cultivation of each other.

The book series I have devoted will consist of 'Qi-Gong theory foundations,' 'Wu-Qin-Xi' (five animal frolics), 'Ba-Duan-Jin' (eight pieces of brocades), 'Yi-Jin-Jing' (the Classic of changing muscle and tendon) and 'Liu-Zi-Jue' (six healing sounds). These are the most popular and widely circulated Qi-Gong life nurturing exercise in the world today. In each book, its origination and development, characteristics and practical points are described in detail. Each movement in the exercise is explained by decomposed descriptions consisting of 'key points,' 'common errors,' 'correct method' and 'effectiveness.' This will greatly help practitioners to get to the correct way of each movement and obtain the promising progress, strengthen the body's immune system, overcome diseases, and reach the goal of longevity.

There are abundant Qi-Gong books available in the market, with 2-D diagram and general descriptions. Many Qi-Gong enthusiasts find it hard to follow because of the disconnection between general illustration and concrete movement. Rooted in my long period of personal practice and coaching experience, I am trying my best to build a bridge between Qi-Gong classic and concrete movements. It took me eight years to shape this book series. I have learned every moment while writing this book. I present the book with concrete and understandable key points, show the reader with detailed teaching strategy. The purpose of this book is to provide Qi-Gong beginners with a solid and practical channel. Practitioners should begin with the basic frame of every movement and try to understand the author's teaching intention through practicing, then gradually reach the state of combination of minds, Qi and body.

I sincerely suggest the learners to combine the text and pictures together, pay attention to the word 'simultaneously' or 'at the same time' when learning the movement for a certain action to ensure the consistency and integrity of the action in practice.

Yajun Zhuang
Baton Rouge, Louisiana
Spring 2019

Acknowledgements

In addition to those who have contributed in large and small ways to accomplish 'Qi Gong Life Nurturing series,' I would like to thank the following people for their efforts. They made the book possible with their professionalisms and skills.

I am grateful to Dr. Li Li, professor in the School of Health and Kinesiology in Georgia Southern University, for his valuable preface and initiating of this book. I owe a great debt to Dr. Elbert Hu, a former senior researcher at Exxon Mobil with profound knowledge in traditional Chinese culture, for his strong support in launching this project and for his insightful comments and guidance along the way, which helped enormously in bringing this book to be fulfilled.

I am especially grateful to my Tai-Chi Qi Gong students Ms. Priscilla P Ashworth, Ms. Shaowei Chen, Ms. Xiaohua Chen, Sharon O'Brien and Kenneth Chow, etc., for helping me organizing, proofreading and reviewing the manuscripts of the book. I thank my friend ChongYang Man and my student Rebecca for taking pictures and editing the illustrations used in the text. If this book could have a small impact on you, the reader, just as these people do to me, I would be a happy Qi-Gong life culture writer.

Dao-Yin Figure	**24 Solar-Terms**	**Health Qi-Gong**
导引图	陈希夷 **24** 气坐功	健身气功

Tiger Play

Deer Play

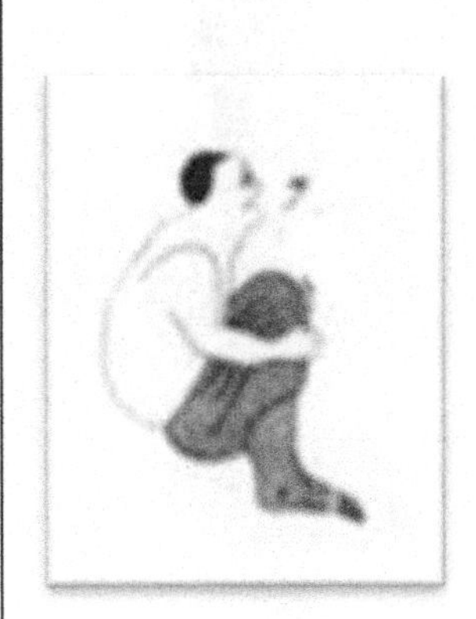

Bear Play

Dao-Yin Figure 导引图 | **24 Solar-Terms** 陈希夷 24 气坐功 | **Health Qi-Gong** 健身气功

Monkey Play

Bird Play

Chapter 1
Introduction of Wu-Qin-Xi

Whenever you feel unwell, rise and do the frolics of mimic-animal and you will soon begin sweating. After applying some power to the body, you will be relieved and feel like eating.
---- Dr. Hua-Tuo

'Wu-Qin-Xi,' is one of the well-known therapeutic sets and the most common forms of ancient Chinese Qi-Gong Life Nurturing used as 'Dao-Yin' technique 导引 (we will discuss it at Chapter 4), as well as the longest-circulating exercise in China. Literally it is translated as 'five animal frolics', which imitates the actions and appearances of animals based on the habits of Tiger, Deer, Bear, Ape or Monkey, and Bird or Crane to build up health and prolong life. It belongs to the 'Dong Qi-Gong' 动气功 (Dynamic Qi-Gong) and was organized into an effective combined set and created by the most famous Chinese medical doctor Hua-Tuo, (A.D. 145-208) 华佗 who lived around 2000 years ago, often called the 'Father of Chinese Medicine.'

There are many legendary stories, passed down from generation to generation, as to how Hua-Tuo cured lots of different difficult and complicated cases of the illness. His principle of resisting the onset of disease by working and doing some exercises was also a major contribution to traditional Chinese Medicine.

He was a miracle medical doctor in the 'East Han Dynasty'东汉 (A.D. 23--220), and 'Three-Kingdom Era' 三国 (A.D.220--265) of China. He was described as looking like 'an immortal that had passed the gates of this life' and 'a man with the complexion of a youth and a snowy beard.' 'The Book of Later Han' 后汉书 records that Hua-Tuo was not only an expert in surgery (according to record, he was the first person in the world to develop the use of anesthesia during surgery); and, he invented the 'Five Animal Frolics' for health preservation and rehabilitation. He thought:

'Human body must have physical exercise but should not exert him/her to the extreme. With the movement of the body, the 'Gu Qi' 谷气 (grain Qi) is digested easily and absorbed completely, and blood circulates smoothly and freely; thus, no disease will occur. This is just like a door-hinge never gets worm-eaten.'

The 'Five animal frolics' advocated by him is a physical fitness exercise conducted by imitating the motions of birds and beasts, which in combination with such training methods as Dao-Yin, 导引 Xing-Qi 行气(we will discuss it at Chapter 4) and Tu-Na 吐纳(expel stagnant Qi and take in the new)expiration and inspiration, promoting the circulation of Qi, etc., It can be employed to train the tendon, the bone, the skin, and the muscle externally and the vital essence, Qi and spirit 精、气、神 internally, thus a rehabilitation method of physical exercise which is compact and well organized with simple and harmonious movements and easy popularization. Based on this exercise, later generations developed quite a few schools with each evolving a different style, all of which spread to other countries of the Asia and other countries in Europe and America.

As a famous Chinese Medicine doctor, Hua-Tuo was proficient at the theories and practices of Dao-Yin, Tu-Na and expiration and inspiration. He believed that this exercise, acting just like physical and breathing exercise, can dispel the diseases and benefit arms and legs. In case of discomfort, a one mimic-animal frolic will make you wet with perspiration so that you apply powder to the body, therefore you feel relaxed and recover the appetite for food.

'Wu-Qin-Xi' can be employed to preserve health and prevent diseases as well as to boost recovery from diseases. According to 'The Life of Hua-Tuo,' who persevered in practicing the 'Five animal frolics', so that 'he still looked vigorous and strong at the age of one hundred.'

Wu-Pu, 吴普 an outstanding disciple of Hua-Tu, lived for over 100 years, and followed this practice every day with the result that 'he could still have good vision and an exquisite sense of hearing and with a full mouth of firm teeth at the age of over ninety.'

'whenever you feel unwell, rise and do the frolics of mimic-animal and you will soon begin sweating and after applying some power to the body you will be relieved and feel like eating.' ---from the records of three kingdoms Wei book Fang-Ji biography

'体有不快，起作一禽之戏，沾濡汗出，因上著粉，身体轻便，腹中饮食'。--源于三国志 魏书方伎传

Modern people believe that mimicking the fierceness of tiger can invigorate the Kidney Qi; mimicking the calmness of bear can relieve the depressed Spleen Qi; mimicking the peacefulness of deer can strengthen the Liver Qi; mimicking the agility of ape or monkey can reinforce the Heart Qi; and mimicking lightness of bird can regulate the Lung Qi.

The relationships of 'Five animals' and 'five solid organs'

Five elements	Wood	Fire	Earth	Gold	Water
Five animals	Deer	Ape	Bear	bird	Tiger
Five Zang	Liver	Heart	Spleen	Lungs	Kidneys

Practitioner can practice all five frolics or pick only one or two to practice, based on his personal physical conditions. During practice, it requires the practitioner to coordinate his/her thoughts, breathing, and movements. If you can practice it persistently, you will enjoy light spirit, enhanced appetite, improved agility, and firm steps. This has the functions of nurturing spirit, regulating the flow of Qi and blood, helping Zang 脏 (Five solid organs—heart, liver, spleen, lungs, and kidneys) and Fu, 腑 (six hollow organs—small intestine, large intestine, stomach, gall, gall bladder, triple burner) opening meridians, 经络 activating sinews and bones, and benefiting joints. The 'Five Animal Frolics' is also effective in preventing and curing lung diseases, asthma, high blood pressure, heart-crown disease, weak nerve system, and indigestion, etc. In addition, frequent practice of the 'Five Animal Frolics' can correct abnormal footings and walking postures, prevent wilting of muscles(amyotrophy), and improve body balance. It is also beneficial to other symptoms. Practitioner should practice for 15 minutes twice daily, one in the morning and one in the evening. Also, the practitioner should select a field with fresh air and luxuriant vegetation.

Chapter 2
Illustration of the Traditional Hua-Tuo 'Five animal frolics'

This set was originally published in 'Yun-Ji-Qi-Jian' (Taoist Canon) 云笈七签 or so called 'Seven slips of the cloudy satchel' in English, which was compiled by Zhang-Jun Fang 张君芳 (Song Dynasty 960--1279). This work is one of the major Taoist anthologies. The sections 12-26, covering volumes 29-86, which is almost half of the entire anthology, deal with the techniques of meditative and gymnastic practices, medical healing, and alchemy. Below is an illustration of the 'Five Animal Frolics' from this work. Even through this exercise may not be the original from Hua-Tuo, it may be rated as one of the earliest documents of the 'Five Animal Frolics' in history. The creeping therapy advocated today looks like the ancient Chinese 'Five animal frolics.' The original text is as follows:

虎戏者：四肢距地，前三掷，却二掷；长引腰，乍却，仰天，即返距行，前,却各七过也。

鹿戏者：四肢距地，引项返顾，左三右二，伸左右，伸缩亦三、亦二也。

熊戏者：正仰，以双手抱膝下，举头，左僻地七，右亦七，蹲地，以手左右托地。

猿戏者：举物自悬，伸缩身体，上下一七；以脚拘物自悬左右七，手钩却立，按头各七。
鸟戏者：双立手，翘一足，伸两臂，扬眉用，各二七；坐伸脚，手挽，足趾各七，缩伸两臂各七也。

Tiger play: *make the palms and feet touching the ground, and then go three steps forward and two steps backward; stretch the waist, and look upward, then return to original position. Do seven times forwards and backwards.*

Deer play: *make the palms and feet touching the ground, stretch the neck and look around, make left turn three times and right turn two times; then stretch the legs backward, also make the left stretch three times and right stretch two times.*

Bear play: *lay down facing up, and hold knees with the hands, look up; twist the body from left to right seven times. Squat down with the butt touching the ground, while using the hands to support the body.*

Ape play: *hold the bar with the hands and hang the body down naturally, then pull-up for seven times; hang the body down by holding the bar with ankles (make the foot hook), lift the upper body up while holding the head with one hand. Do seven times each side.*

Bird play: *stand up and stretch arms to the sides with fingers up while lifting one foot forward with the toes up and rising the eyebrows. Seven times each foot. Sit up with legs stretching forward, then reach the hands to touch the toes, repeat seven times. Finally stretch the arm above the head for seven times.*

The detailed practice of 'Hua Tuo's Wu-Qin-Xi' is as follows:

Wuji Standing (Start Form)
无极桩

(1) Stand upright with your feet at shoulder width apart and parallel to each other. The weight of your body should be evenly distributed between both feet and between the ball and heel of each foot.

(2) Keep your knees straight, but not locked (do not pull the kneecap up nor push the knees back). Sink your shoulders and drop your elbows. Let your arms hang down in a relaxed manner at your sides with palms facing the thighs.

Figure 6.1

(3) Relax your neck and keep your head vertical, as if suspended by a string tied to the 'Crown Point' at the top of your head. Tuck your chin in slightly.

(4) The mouth is closed with lips and teeth lightly touching each other. The tongue slightly touches the roof of your mouth.
(5) Gently contract your hips and pull up the muscles at the back of your thighs. Tuck your tailbone into your body (nudge the pelvis slightly forward). Your pelvis feels light on the tops of your thighs. Without tensing your stomach muscles, move them up and slight inward.
(6) Relax your whole body into the ground, balanced and stable like a mountain. Look straight ahead into infinity with a soft and wide-angle focus.
(7) Concentrate your mind on your 'Dantian,' and visualize that the warmth and the brightness surround there and full of Qi. Regulate your breathing and keep it full but natural. It is best to breathe through the nose, as the tiny hairs and mucous membranes filter out dust and toxins from the air. (See Figure 6.1)

First Frolic: Tiger Play
虎戏

(1) From the start form, as you are inhaling, raise your arms forward at shoulder width apart and shoulder height. Palms down. Look straight ahead. (See Figure 6.2)

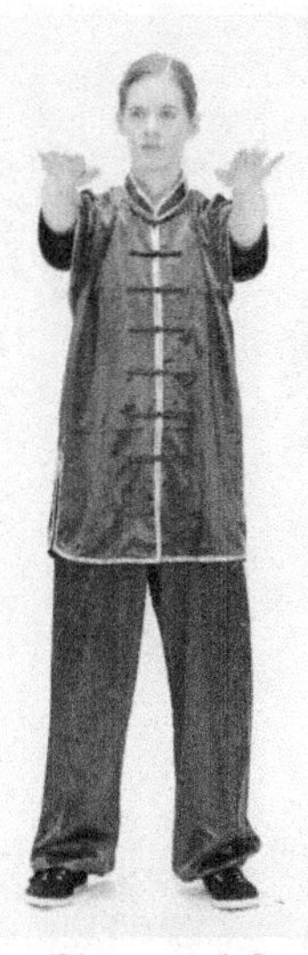

Figure 6.2

(2) When exhaling, bend your waist forward and slowly squat down just like a tiger (this varies based on your body's condition, you can choose to bend your knees or stretch your knees). Bring your both palms to the floor directly in front of your feet. Take a deep breathing. Look down in the front. (See Figure 6.3)
(3) When inhaling, lift your heels as high as possible and move your trunk forward and extend your arms, and slowly shift your weight to your palms. Now you should feel the all fingers and toes deeply

pressing against into the ground. Look down in the front. Stay for a moment. (See Figure 6.4)

(4) When you exhale, move your trunk back as far as possible. Press your fingers into the ground and pull your thighs, shoulders and hip backward while extending your sides of the body and spine. Look backward. Stay for a moment. (See figure 6.5)

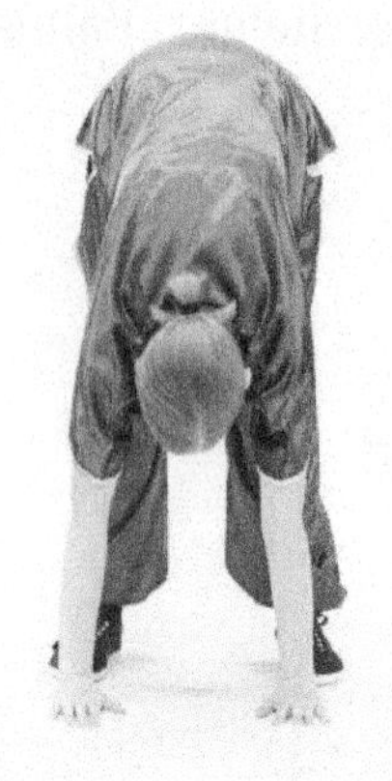

Figure 6.3 (face)

Figure6.3 (side)

Figure 6.4(side)

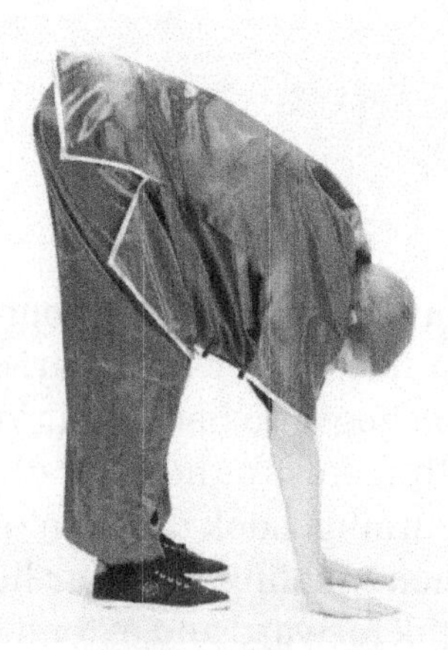

Figure 6.5(side)

Repeat movement (3) and (4) three times. Then

(5) As you are inhaling, move your body forward with your palms, like a tiger walking three steps forward, forming a 'push-ups' posture. (See Figure 6.6, 6.7, 6.8,) And then stretch your whole body and low your waist down. Straighten your arms and lengthen your spine. Keep your tiptoes touching the floor, but keep your hips, thighs, and shins off the floor. Look upward. (See Figure 6.9) Stay still for a while.

Figure 6.6(side)

Figure 6.7(side)

Figure 6.8(side)

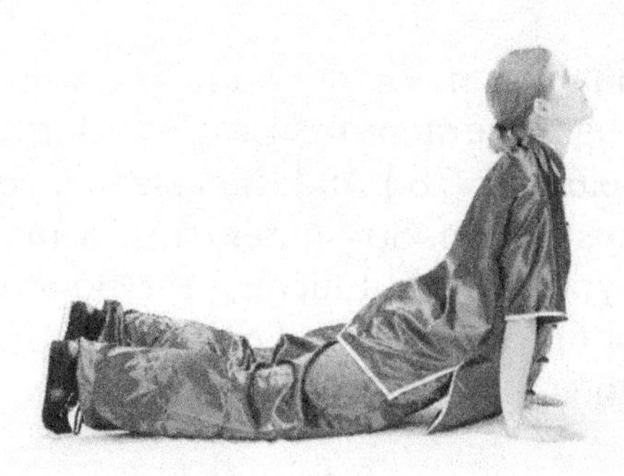

Figure 6.9(side)

(6) As you are exhaling, put your palms on the floor, and extend the top of your head forward. Connect abdominal muscles to a parallel line. Be careful not to make your hips higher than your lower back or sink to the floor. Now look down. (See Figure 6.10) Stay still for a while.

Figure6.10

Repeat movement (5) and (6) seven times. Then

(7) As you are inhaling, move your body backward with your palms to return (2) posture. And then take an exhaling. Stay still for a while. Regulate your breathing. Look downward. (See Figure 6.11, 6.12, 6.13)

Figure 6.11

Figure 6.12

Figure 6.13

(8) As you are inhaling, gradually get your upper body up, turn your arms outward and raise them on both side of your body. (See Figure 6.14) until they are above your head. Palms facing the Crown Point. Look straight ahead. (See Figure 6.15)
(9) As you are exhaling, press your palms down passing your face in front of your Dan-Tian area. Still look straight ahead. (See Figure 6.16) and then slowly drop your arms down and return to the preparation position. (See Figure 6.17)

Figure 6.14

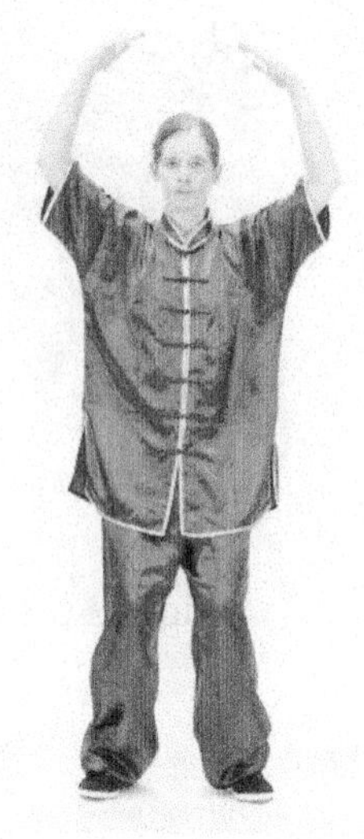

Figure 6.15

Figure 6.16

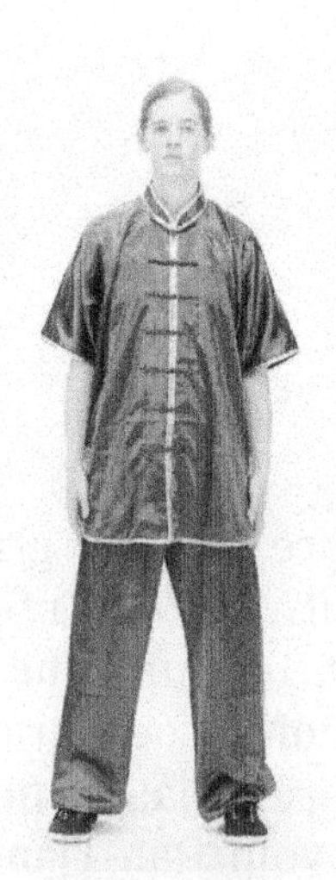

Figure 6.1

Tiger Play

Dao

Second Frolic: Deer Play
鹿戏

(1) Connect the previous movement. As you are inhaling, raise your arms forward at shoulder width apart and shoulder height. Palms down. Look straight ahead. (See figure 6.18)

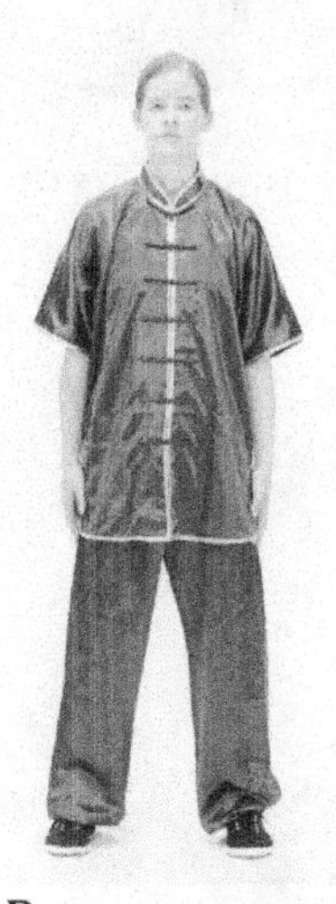

Pre-movement

Figure 6.18

(2) As you are exhaling, bend your waist forward and slowly and gently squat down. Bring your both palms to the floor directly in front of your feet. Whole palms and soles should touch the floor. Take a deep breathing. Look down in the front. (See Figure 6.19)
(3) As you are inhaling, expand your neck like a deer and turn your head slowly to the left as far as possible. Look back at the shoulder

on the left. Stay still for a while and hold your breathing. (See Figure 6.20)

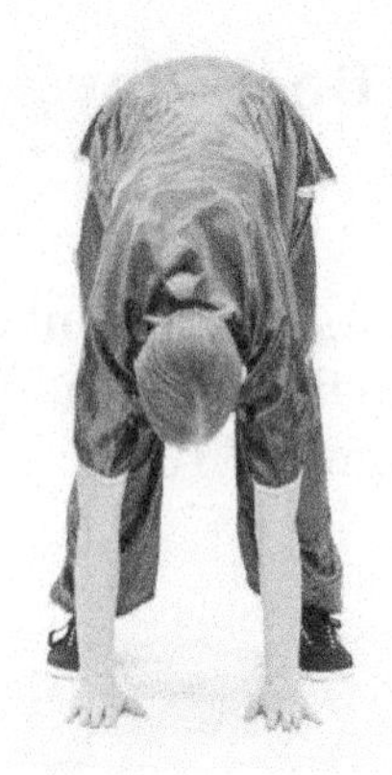

Figure 6.19(face)

Figure 6.19(side)

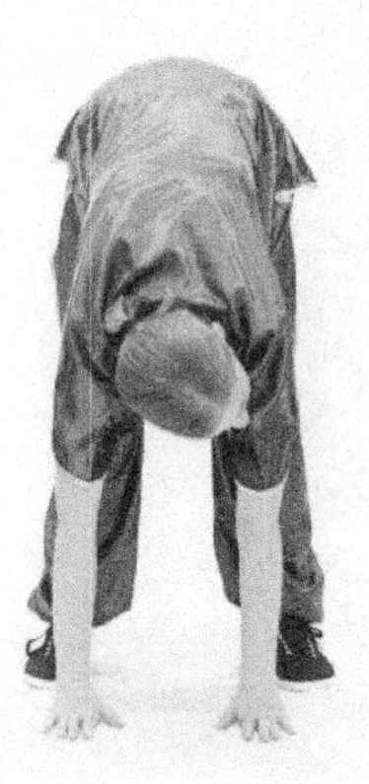

Figure 6.20

Figure 6.21

Figure 6.22

(4) As you are exhaling, loose your neck and gently return your head back to look down in the front. (See Figure 6.21)
(5) When your face is down, take a deep inhalation slowly. Now you need to stretch your neck again and slowly turn your head to the

right as far as possible. Look back at the shoulder on the right. Stay still for a while and hold your breathing. (See Figure 6.22)

Repeat movement (3) to (5). Following the traditional method, look back to the left 3 times and to the right 2 times. Finally return to the (Figure 6.19) posture. Then

(6) As you are inhaling, stretch your left knee as far as possible, and lift your left leg to the air behind you. Keep your standing leg (right leg) slightly bent, and place your right foot rooted into the floor. (See Figure 6.23)
(7) As you are exhaling, put your left leg down to its original position. Look ahead. (See Figure 6.24)
(8) As you are inhaling, stretch your right knee as far as possible, and lift your right leg to the air behind you. Keep your standing leg (left leg) slightly bent, and place your left foot rooted into the floor. (See Figure 6.25)

Figure 6.23

Figure 6.24(side)

(9) As you are exhaling, put your right leg down to its original position. Look straight ahead. (See Figure 6.26)

Repeat (6) to (9). left leg 3 times and right leg 2 times. Then

(10) As you are inhaling, gradually raise your upper body up, lift your arms forward and upward until they are above your head.

(See Figure 6.27, 6.28) Slightly stretch your elbows, place your palms outward. Look straight ahead.

(11) As you are exhaling, separate your arms and slowly push your palms down to the sides of your hips. Look straight ahead. (See Figure 6.29)

Figure 6.25(side)

Figure 6.26(side)

Figure 6.27

Figure 6.28

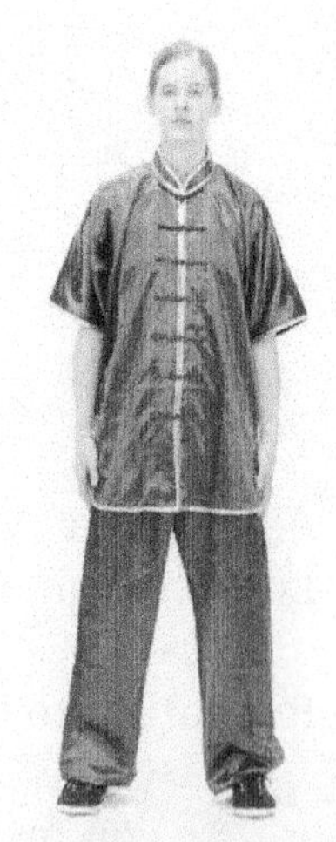

Figure 6.29

The Figures of the Continuous Movements

Deer Play

Jing Qi-Shen
Essence, Chi and Spirit

Third Frolic: Bear Play
熊戏

(1) Lie on the floor on your back, with your legs and arms fully stretched, and your feet parallel to each other. Take a few deep breathings. (See Figure 6.30)
(2) As you inhale, lift your upper body gently and bend your knees, hug them to your chest and let your feet leave the floor. Now, you should raise up your head and arch the back. (See Figure 6.31)

Figure 6.30

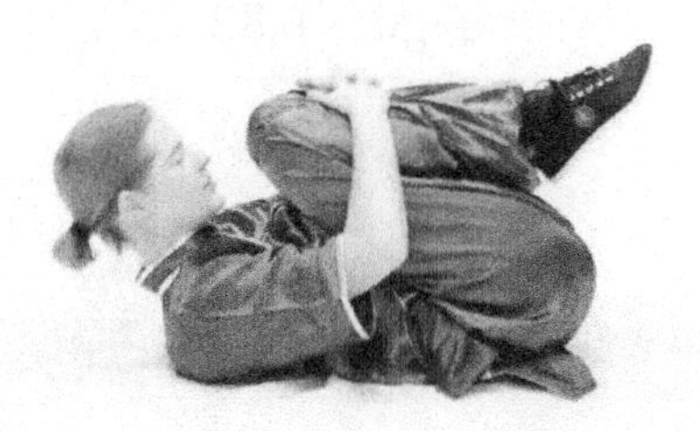

Figure 6.31

(3) Release your whole body and lie on the floor, let your legs and arms fully stretched, make your feet parallel. Take a few deep breathings and imagine your Dan-Tian into the floor. (See Figure 6.32)

Figure 6.32

Repeat (2) to (3) 7 times. Then

(4) As you inhale, bend your knees and hold them with both hands, while rolling your whole body smoothly to the left, balancing your left hip against the floor and keeping your feet off the floor. Look at left. (See Figure 6.33)
(5) As you exhale, release your whole body and lie on the floor, let your legs and arms fully stretched, and feet parallel. (See Figure 6.34)

Figure 6.33

Figure 6.34

(6) As you inhale, bend your knees and hold them with both hands, while rolling your whole body smoothly to the right, balancing your right hip against the floor and keeping your feet off the floor. Look right. (See Figure 6.35)

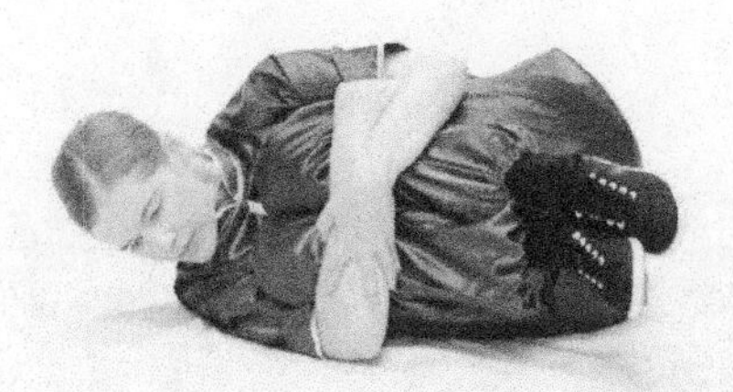

Figure 6.35

(7) As you exhale, release your whole body and lie on the floor, let your legs and arms fully stretched, and feet parallel. Take a few deep breathings. (See Figure 6.36)

Figure 6.36

Repeat (4) to (7) 7 times each side. Then

(8) Sit up and make a 'full squat' posture, with your hips and palms touching the floor. (See Figure 6. 37)
(9) When you inhale, wobble your body to the right while lifting your left leg with your left hand holding and hugging the left knee close your chest. (See Figure 6.38)
(10) When you exhale, wobble your body to the left while lifting your right leg and hugging the right knee close your chest. (See Figure 6.39)

Figure 6.37.

Figure 6.38

Figure 6.39

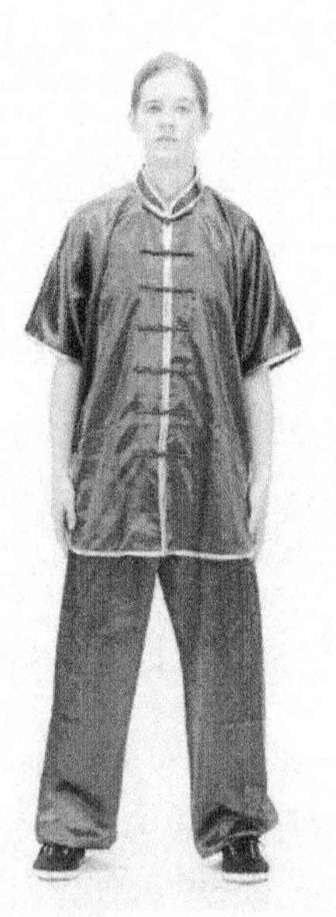

Figure 6.40

Repeat (9) to (10) 7 times each side. Then

Stand up forming the 'preparation position.' (See Figure 6.40)

The Figures of the Continuous Movement

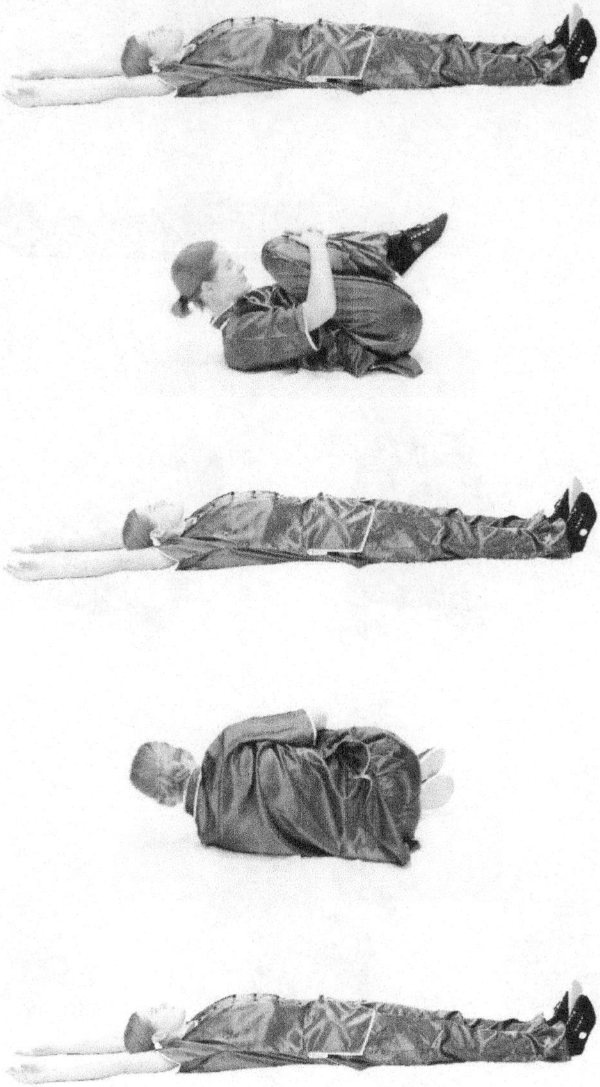

Bear Play

Fourth frolic: Monkey play
猴戏

Choose a strong pole like horizontal bar. Basically, it should be higher than your body, or you can reach it with your fingers while standing.

(1) Stand upright, and then hold the pole with your hands, and your body will hang down naturally. Stay for a moment following your body's condition. (See Figure 6.41)
(2) Then do chin-up 7 times. (See Figure 6.42)

Figure 6.41　　　Figure 6.42

(3) After that, lift your legs, hook the pole with your feet, (See Figure 6.43) let your body drop naturally, and hold your head with your palms. Stay still for a while and take a few breathings. (See Figure6.44)

(4) Then grab the pole with your right hand and massage your 'jade pillow' 7 times with your left hand. (See Figure 6. 45)
(5) Keep the feet hooking and switch your left hands to hold the pole, massage your 'jade pillow' 7 times with right hand. (See Figure 6.46)

Figure 6.43 Figure 6.44

Figure 6.45 Figure 6.46

If you can't practice this 'Play' according to your physical condition, you can substitute with following movements to do it:

(1) Lie on your back on the floor with your legs and arms fully extended in the opposite direction, feet parallel. look at the sky. (See Figure 6.47)
(2) When inhaling, sit up slowly and raise your arms above your head (See Figure 6.48), then hold your fists and gently pull them down to the shoulders and bend your knees. Turn around and look at the left. (See Figure 6.49)

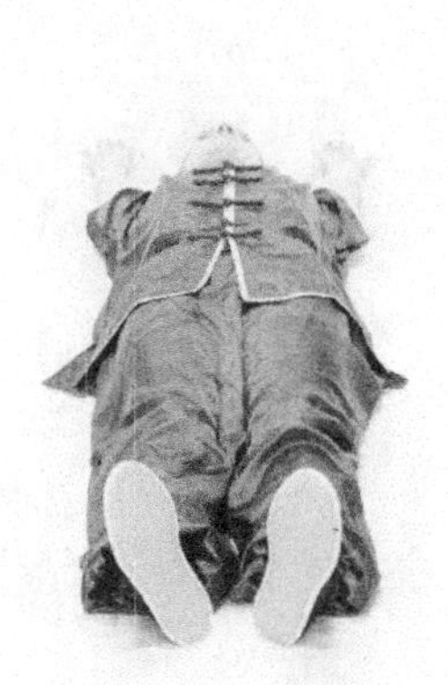

Figure 6.47

Figure 6.48

Figure 6.49

(3) When exhaling, smoothly return to lay down position. Look at upward. (See Figure 6.50)
(4) When inhaling, sit up slowly and raise your arms above your head (See Figure 6.51), then hold your fists and gently pull them down to the shoulders and bend the knees. Turn around and look at the right. (See Figure 6.52)

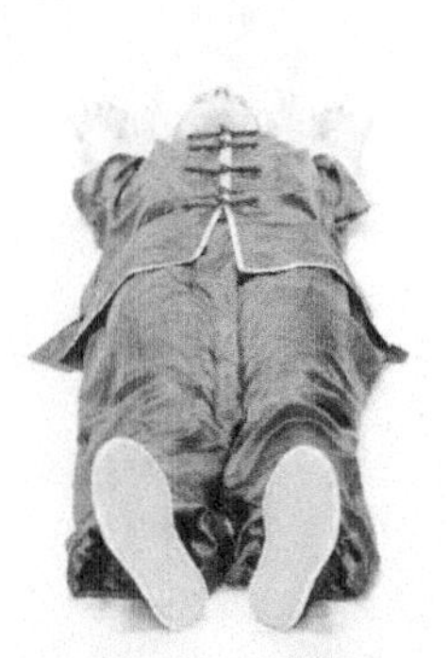
Figure 6.50

Figure 6.51

Figure 6.52

Repeat 7 times each side. Then

(5) Stand up with your feet at shoulder width apart. (See Figure 6.53)

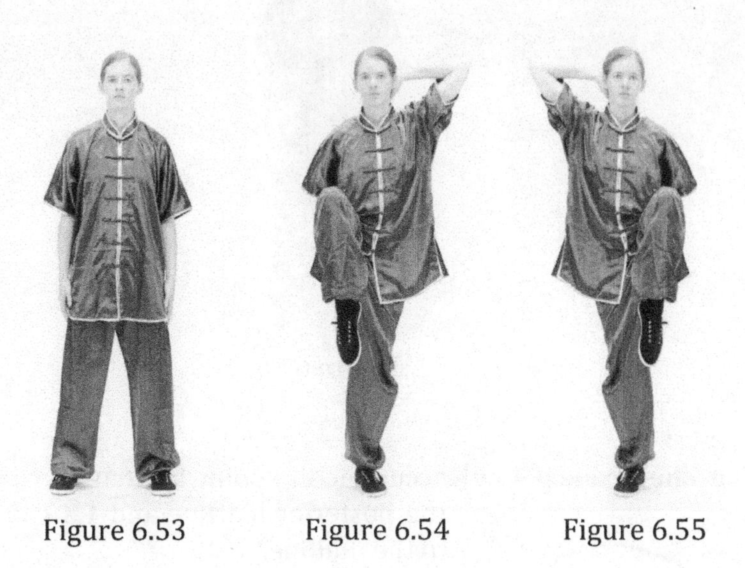

Figure 6.53 Figure 6.54 Figure 6.55

(6) Holding your 'Yu-Zhen' (Jade Pillow) with your left palm; placing your right hand behind your body and touching the 'Ming-Men.' (Gate of Life) Palm outward. At the same time, standing on the left leg (lift your right leg). Massage your 'jade pillow' and 'Ming-Men' with your hands clockwise 7 times and counterclockwise 7 times. (See figure 6.54)

(7) Then holding your 'Yu-Zhen' with your right palm; placing your left hand behind your body and touching the 'Ming-Men.' Palm outward. At the same time, standing on the right leg (lift your left leg). Massage your 'jade pillow' and 'gate of life' with your hands clockwise 7 times and counterclockwise 7 times. (See Figure 6.55)

(8) Return to the preparation position. (See Figure 6.56)

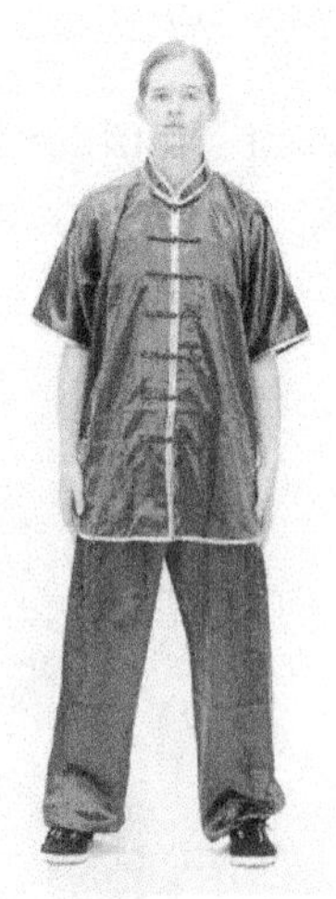

Figure 6.56

Note:

- **Yu-Zhen** (jade pillow): accupuncture point, located 2.5 cun above the posterior hairline and 1.3 cun lateral to the midline.

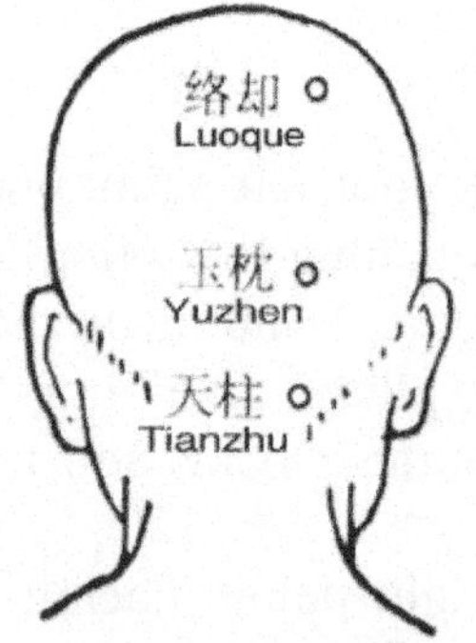

- **Ming-Men** (Gate of Life): It is an acupuncture point located between the kidneys, which are the place where 'Zhen Qi' accumulate. It is the source of life, the lord of fire, and the depot of essence Qi. Qi and Ming-Men is the root of the human being. If the root is gone, then ZangFu, or internal organs, tendons, and Meridians will wilt and rot.

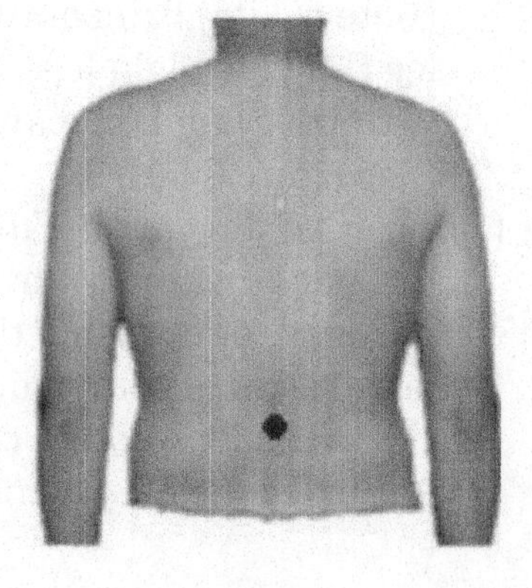

The Figures of the Continuous Movements

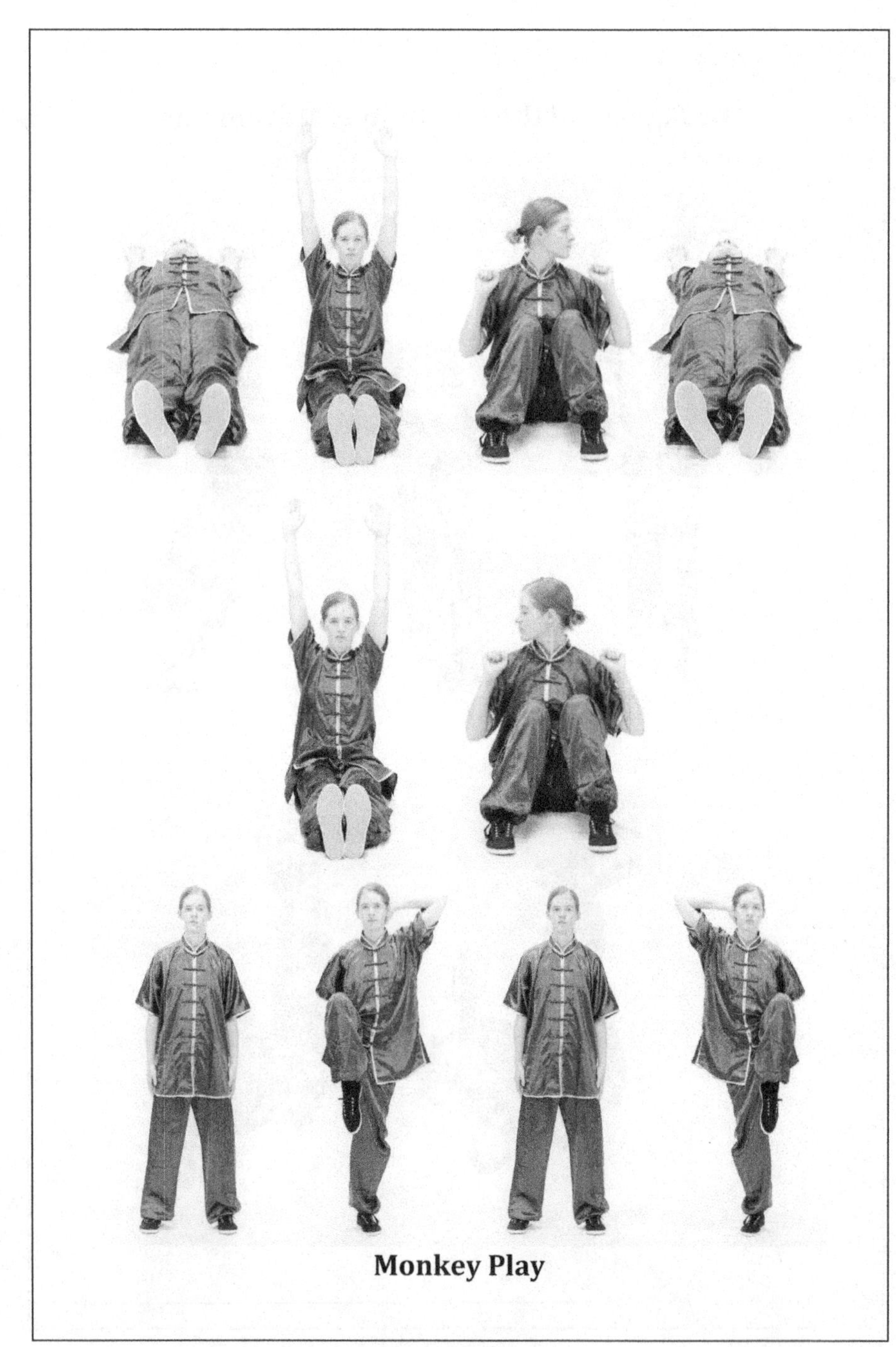

Monkey Play

Fifth frolic: Bird play
鸟戏

(1) Connect the previous movement, on an inhale, extend your arms forward and upward, (See Figure 6.57 (2), 6.58) and then separate your palms to the sides of your body. Palms out, fingers up and arms at shoulder height. (See Figure 6.59) At the same time, lift your left leg to your abdomen height. Hook up the left toes. Now you should raise your eyebrows elegantly and delicately as if a real crane was flying. (See Figure 6.60.) Stay still for a while following your condition. Look straight ahead.

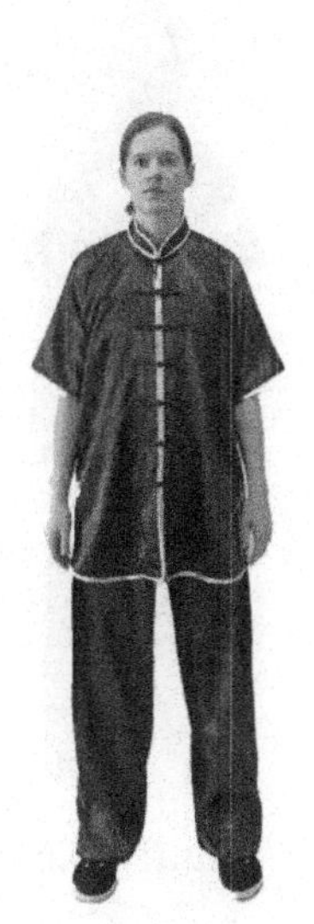
Previous movement

Figure 6.57

Figure 6.58

Figure 6.59

Figure 6.60

Figure 6.61

(2) As you exhale, drop your arms and left leg to return the starting position. (See Figure 6.61.)

On an inhale, extend your arms forward and upward, (See Figure 6.62, 6.63) and then separate your palms to the sides of your body. Palms out, fingers up and arms at shoulder height. (See Figure 6.64) At the same time, lift your right leg into your abdomen height. Hook up the right toes. Now you should raise your eyebrows elegantly and delicately as if a real crane was flying. (See Figure 6.65) Stay still for a while following your condition. Look straight ahead.

Figure 6.62

Figure 6.63

Figure 6.64

Figure 6.65

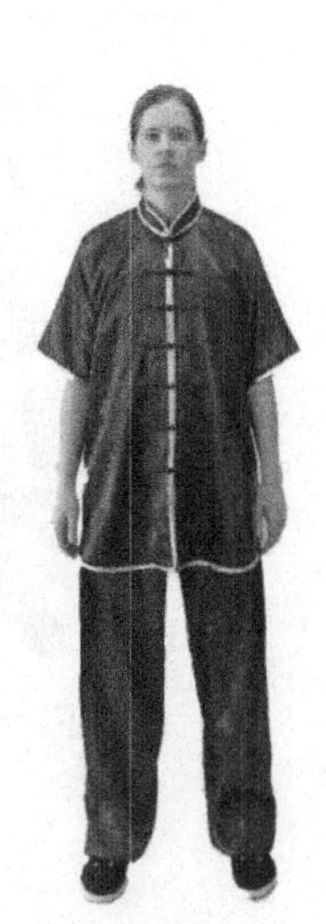

Figure 6.66

(3) As you exhale, drop your arms and right leg to return the starting position. (See Figure 6.66)

Repeat 7 times each side. Then

(4) Sit down and extend your legs on the floor. Toes up. Regulate your breathing. (See Figure 6.67)

Figure 6.67

Figure6.678

Figure 6.69

Figure 6.70

(5) When you inhale, relax your left leg, bend your right knee to touch your chest while using your hands to tightly hold your soles. (See figure 6.68) Stay still for a while.

(6) When you exhale, extend your right leg on the floor gently. Toes up. (See figure 6.69)

(7) When you inhale, relax your right leg, bend your left knee to touch your chest while using your hands to hold your soles tightly. (See figure 6.70) Stay still for a while.

Repeat 7 times each side. Finally

(8) Stand up, with your feet at shoulder width apart. Regulate your breathing. (See figure 6.71)

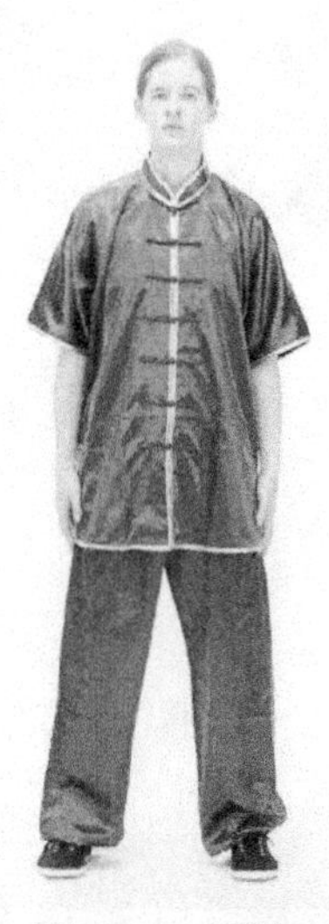

Figure 6.71

(9) On an inhale, rotate your arms outside and raise hands at your sides until they are above your head, palms are facing the Crown Point. Look up. (See figure 6.72, 6.73)

(10) As you exhale, press your palms down past your face to your Dntian area. Look down in the front. (See figure 6.74)

Do 7 times

(11) Then hang your arms down naturally to return original position. (See figure 6.75)

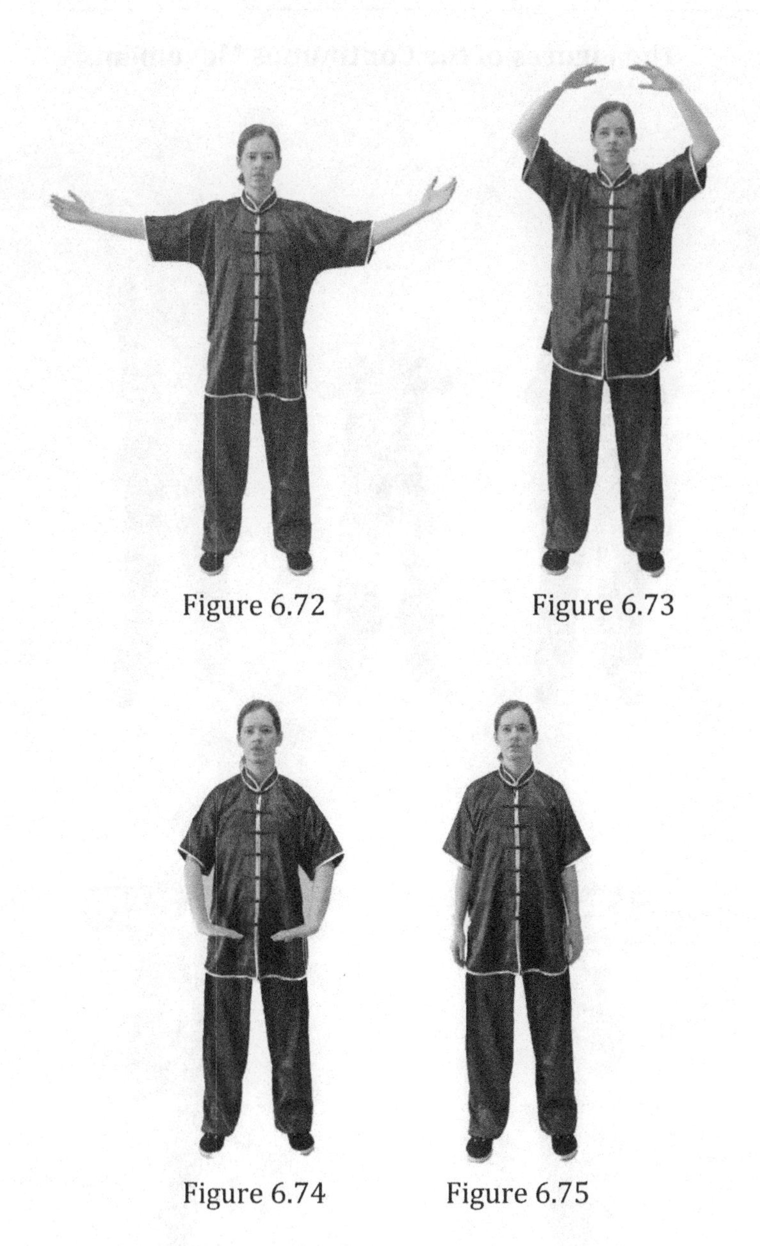

Figure 6.72 Figure 6.73

Figure 6.74 Figure 6.75

If you want to live a long and healthy life like Hua Tuo, over 100 years old, you might as well practice five animal frolics more and more

The Figures of the Continuous Movements

Bird Play

Chapter 3

Health Qi-Gong • 'Five animal frolics'

This set was published in 'Jian-Shen Qi-Gong' 健身气功 or so called 'Health Qi-Gong' in English, which was compiled by China National Sports Commission in 2003, and spread around the world. Detailed explanation of the movements---

Start Form and Regulate Breathing
起势调息

Movement 1

Stand upright with your feet together naturally.

Let your arms hang down in a relaxed manner at the thighs.

Relax your chest and abdomen, suspend your head up and erect your neck. Slightly tuck your chin inward. Place the tongue tip reaching the upper palate.

Focus your mind on your Dan-Tian.

Look straight ahead. (See Figure 7.1)

Movement 2

Relax your whole body rooted into the ground.

Slowly and lightly shift the weight to your right leg. In the meantime, gently lift your left leg and take a step to the left, about shoulder width apart to form the 'Wu-Ji standing'.

Now slightly bend your knees and maintain the state of tranquility.

Regulate your breathing several times (basically about 6 times) and concentrate your mind on the lower Dan-Tian.

Look straight ahead. (See Figure 7.2(1), 7.2(2))

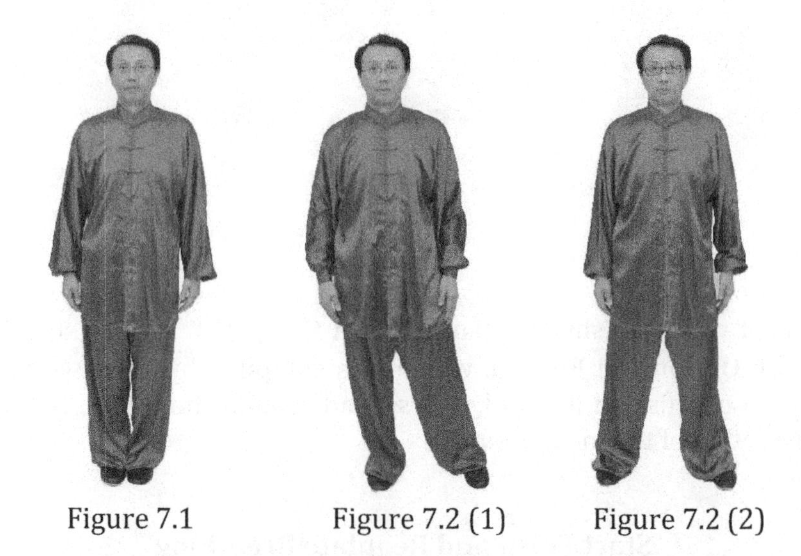

Figure 7.1 Figure 7.2 (1) Figure 7.2 (2)

Specific Requirements of the 'Wu-Ji Standing'

Feet

(1) Place the feet shoulder width apart.
(2) Basically, point toes forward and feet parallel to each other for men and slightly splay outward of toes for women. (See Figure 7.2(3), 7.2(4))
(3) Relax the whole body into the ground, balanced and stable like a mountain.
(4) Make sure that the weight of your body should be evenly distributed between both feet and between the ball and heel of each foot.

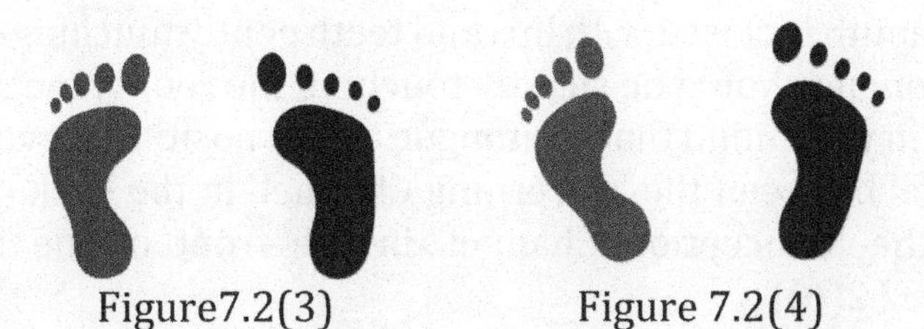

Figure7.2(3) Figure 7.2(4)

Knees

(1) Keep the knees straight and soft, but not locked.

(2) Do not pull the kneecap up nor push the knees back in order to ensure free flow of the blood and Qi.

Hips

(1) Gently contract the hips and pull up the muscles at the back of the thighs.

(2) Tuck the tailbone into the body and nudge the pelvis slightly forward and on the tops of the thighs.

Shoulders and elbows

(1) Sink the shoulders and drop the elbows.

(2) Relax the neck and keep the head vertical, as if suspended by a string tied to the 'Crown Point' 百会穴 at the top of the head. (See Figure 7.2(5))

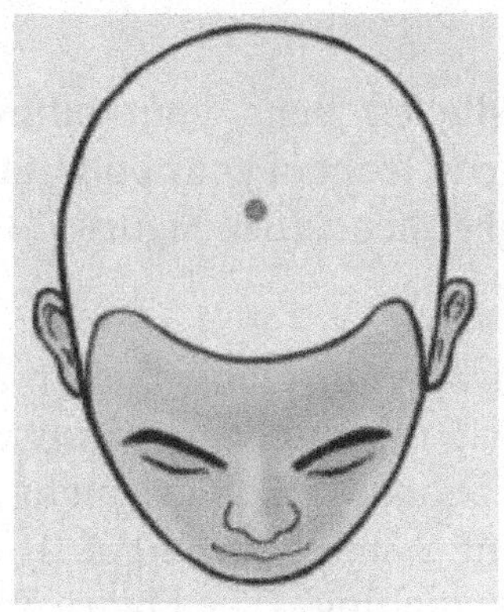

Figure 7.2(5)

Head

(1) The mouth is closed with lips and teeth gently touching each other.
(2) The tongue should be slightly touching the roof of the mouth.
(3) Keep in your mind that the tongue at this position serves as a 'Bird Bridge' between the 'Governing Channel' in the back of the body and the 'Conception Channel' in the front of the body. (See Figure7.2(6))
(4) Tuck the chin in slightly.

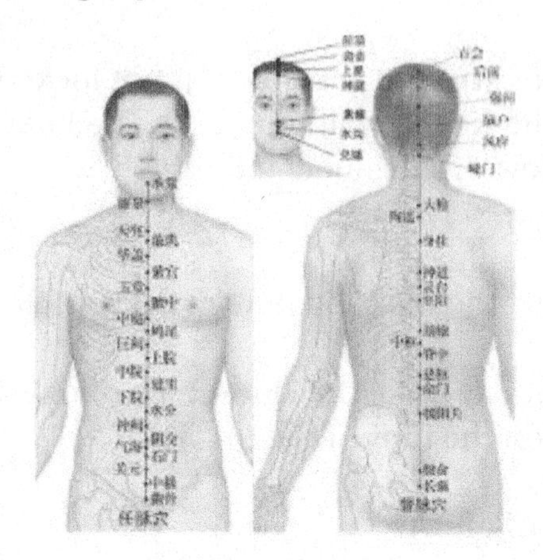

Figure7.2(6)

Eyes

(1) Do not focus eyes on any particular object.
(2) Look straight ahead into infinity with a soft and wide-angle focus.

Movement 3

While inhaling, slightly bend your elbows and raise the palms upward and forward in front of your body, at your chest height. Palms face up. Look straight ahead. (See Figure 7.3)

Movement 4

While exhaling, drop your elbows down and slightly extend them outward while slowly rotating your palms inward and then pushing them down to your abdomen. Look straight ahead. (See Figure 7.4)

Repeat 'movement 3 and movement 4' about 4 times and then return to the 'Wu-Ji standing'. (See Figure 7.5)

Look straight ahead.

Figure 7.3 Figure 7.4 Figure 7.5

Key points

(1) See nothing and hear nothing to keep your calm and quiet.
(2) The movement should be even, slow, soft and coherent.
(3) Regulate your breathing and eliminate all distractive thoughts in your mind.

Intention

Focus the mind on 'Lao-gong' acupoint while raising and pushing. (See Figure 7.6)

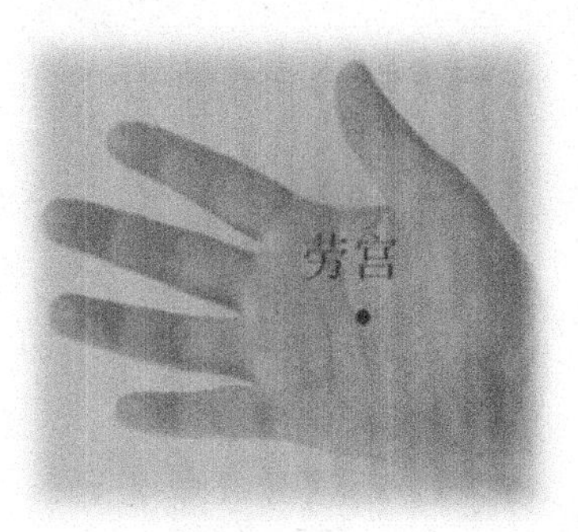

Figure 7.6

Common errors

(1) When stepping outside with your left foot, stretch out both knees too much, and cause the whole body to swing from left to right.

(2) When raising and pushing your palms, the moving route of your palms is not circular, causing the elbows to extend out and the shoulders to shrug up.

Corrections

(1) Before stepping outside, the practitioner should slightly bend the knees first; while stepping outside, the practitioner should shift the weight onto the right leg, after raising the left foot, then slowly and gradually shift the weight onto the left, place the sole of the left foot touching the ground to maintain the balance of the weight.

(2) Consciously sink the shoulders and drop the elbows, then start raising the palms up.

(3) Make sure that every movement including rising, closing and pushing are circular. Smooth and natural.

Effects and functions

(1) Eliminating all distracting thoughts will guide the practitioner into entering the tranquility state. Regulate breathing and relieve uneasiness of mind.

(2) Expelling the old Qi, drawing in the new, will ascend clear Qi and descend stagnant Qi. Nurse the functional activities of the vital Qi.

First Frolic: Tiger Play
虎戏

Features and life nurturing theory

The order of the 'Five animal frolics' are tiger, deer, bear, ape, and bird. The first frolic is 'Tiger Play,' which is to imitate the shape and movement of a tiger. The features of a tiger are its ferocity, strong body, and ability to jump and claw. The most important element in 'Tiger Play' is to imitate the awe-inspiring attitude or the frightful appearance of a tiger. Its spirit is shown in its eyes and its awesomeness comes out of its claws. It gazes with raged eyes and moves like the wind and cloud. It twists its waist with force, wags head and swings tail, and vibrates its body.

In practicing 'Tiger Play,' the practitioners need to focus attention on the 'Ming-Men' (gate of life) acupoint. (See Figure 7.7) It is where the '*Yuan Yang*' (original yang) resides. It is the sea of sperm and blood, the root of '*Yuan Qi*' (original Qi), and the tabernacle of water and fire.

If practitioner focuses attention on the 'gate of life' during practice, it will benefit the kidneys and strengthen the lower back, build the bones and produce marrow. It can also open the Ren-Mai 任脉 (Conception Meridian) and Du-Mai 督脉 (Governor Meridian) to get rid of 'wind pathogens.' 风邪 'Tiger Play' is suitable for curing the following diseases: clogged meridians, numbness caused by partially blocked Qi and blood circulation, pain in pelvis nerves, waist and lower back pain, infected spine, high blood pressure, and infected Du Meridian.

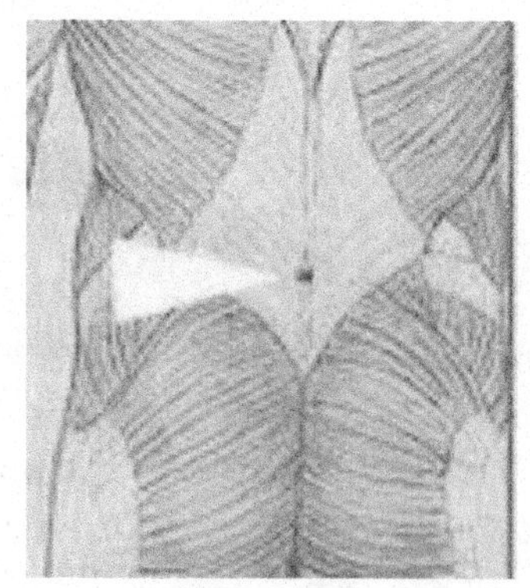

Figure 7.7

Note

(1) **Yuan Yang**: the physiology term, or so-called kidney yang, it is the original source of life.

(2) **Yuan Qi**: it is also called original Qi, or true Qi. It is the basic and most important Qi in human body and is the motivating power in human life activities.

Tiger Lifting
虎举

Movement 1

From the 'Wu-Ji Standing,' slowly turn your palms down from the sides of the body, separating the fingers out and then gradually bend them forming the 'tiger claw.' Look at the hands. (See Figure 7.8(1)(2))

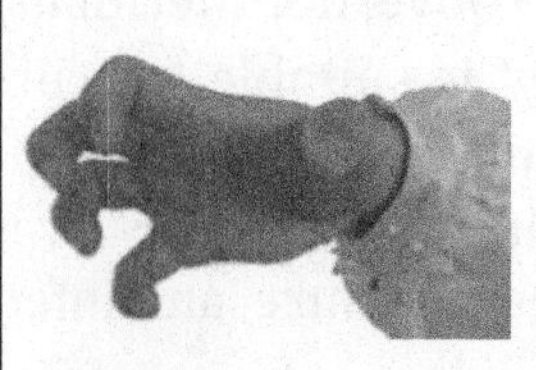

Extend all five fingers and open the tiger-mouth (the web between thumb and index finger). Bend the first and second knuckles inward to imitate tiger strengthening paw.

Wu-Ji Standing Figure 7.8(1) Figure 7.8 (2)

Movement 2

Then rotate your both hands outward, and gradually grasp the fists from the pinkie, ring, middle and index finger. Now, raise the fists up along the sides of the body until they reach the shoulders. (See Finger 7.9(1)(2)(3))

Finger 7.9(1) Finger 7.9(2) Finger 7.9(3)

After that, release the fists into the palms and turn the palms up and raise them above the head, bending the fingers to form the 'tiger claw' again. Look at the hands. (See Figure 7.9(4))

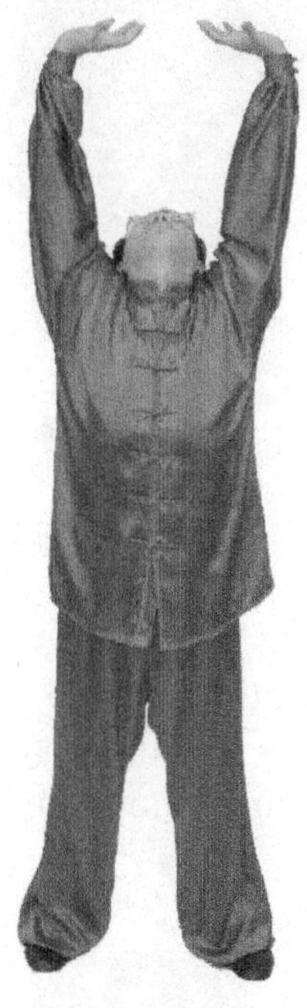

Figure7.9(4)

Movement 3

Follow the previous movement, rotate the palms outward and grasp the fists with the palms. Place both fist-hearts facing each other above the head. Look at the fists. (See Figure 7.10(1)(2))

Pull both fists downward to the shoulders and then release the fists into the palms (See Figure 7.10(3)) and push them down in front of the abdomen. Separate the fingers, with palms down. Look at the hands. (See Figure 7.10(4))

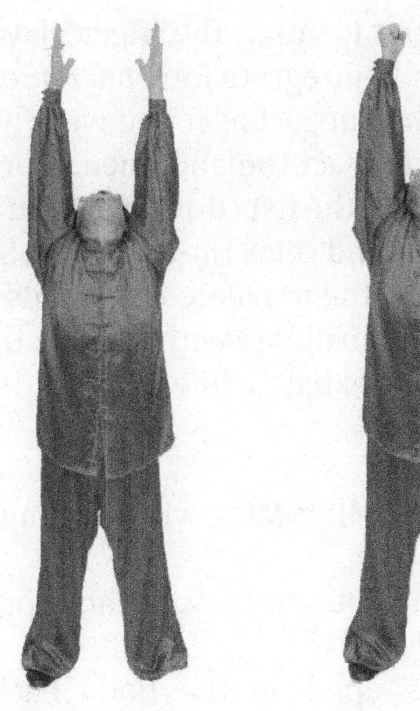

Figure 7.10(1) Figure 7.10(2)

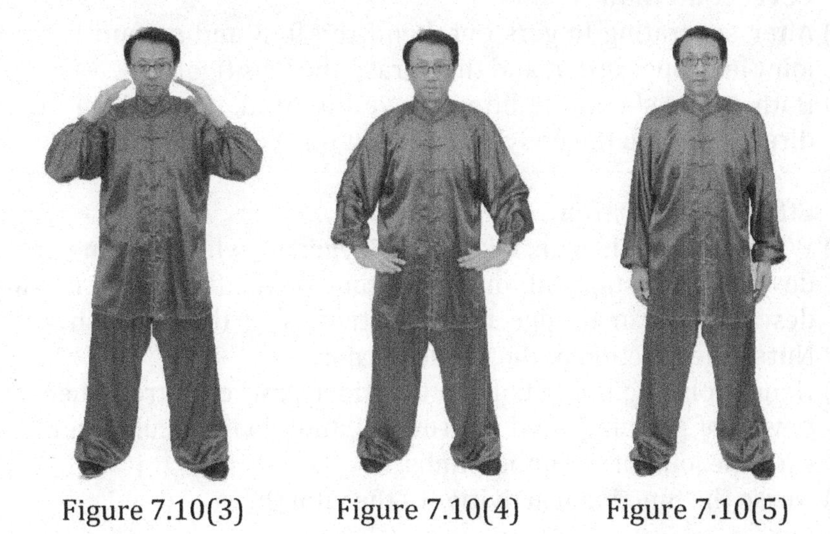

Figure 7.10(3) Figure 7.10(4) Figure 7.10(5)

Repeat movement 1 to 4 about 3 times and then naturally hang the arms down beside the body. Look straight ahead. (See Figure 7.10 (5))

Key points

(1) Separating the fingers, forming the 'tiger claw' and holding the fists; all of these should integrate internal force.
(2) When raising the palms up, act as if you were lifting a heavy staff, raise the chest and contract the abdomen. Elongate to the fullest extent of your body. Pull the fists down as if you are pulling double rings, hollow the chest and relax the abdomen. Sink Qi to Dan-Tian.
(3) The eyes should follow the movement of hands during practice.
(4) The movement could coordinate with the breathing. Basically, you can inhale while rising; exhale while pushing down.

Intention

Focus the mind on the 'Ming-Men' while raising and pushing.

Common errors

(1) Switch hands into the fists directly, without passing through the 'tiger paw.'
(2) When raising palms up, lean the body backward to form a reversed arch.

Correct method

(1) After separating fingers out, bend the first and second knuckle joint in proper order, and then grasp the fists tightly.
(2) Both palms should be lifted above the head, do not lean in any direction. Keep the body in a straight line vertical to the ground.

Effect and function

(1) When lifting palms up, take fresh oxygen in; when pushing palms down, expel stagnant out. One time ascending and one-time descending can dredge the Qi activities of the 'triple burner.' Nurse the function of the 'triple burner.'
(2) Hands forming the fists from the 'tiger paw' can strengthen 'the power of gripping,' and improve Qi and blood circulation of the extreme joint of the upper limbs.
(3) Nurse the functional activities of the vital Qi.

Tiger Pouncing
虎扑

Movement 1

Connect the previous movement, hold the hollow fists with your hands and raise them up along the sides of your body until they rest close to your shoulders. (See Figure 7.11(1)(2)(3))

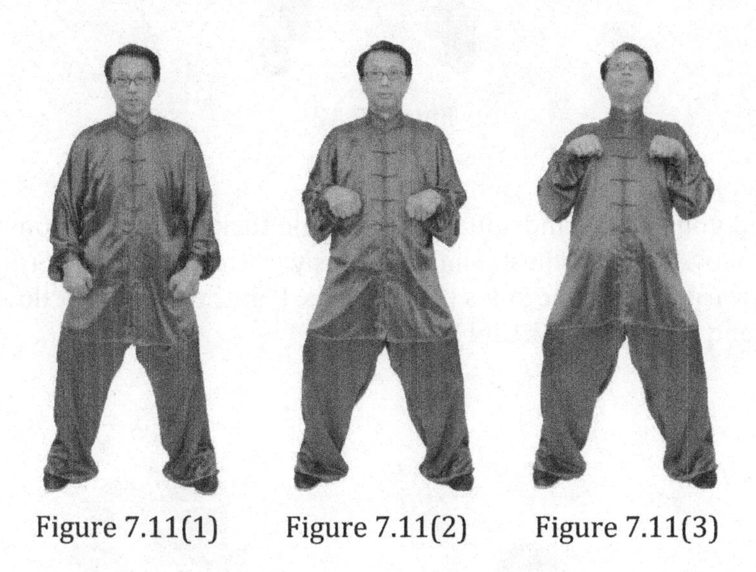

Figure 7.11(1) Figure 7.11(2) Figure 7.11(3)

Movement 2

Continue the previous movement.

Circle your hands upward and forward from your shoulders, bending your fingers to form the 'tiger paw.' Palms down. Meanwhile, bend your upper body forward, stretch your chest and settle your waist. Look straight ahead. (See Figure 7.12)

Figure 7.12

Movement 3

Bend your knees and squat down, while tucking your abdomen in and hollowing your chest. Simultaneously circle the both 'tiger paws' downward toward the sides of the knees. Palms down. Look down in the front. (See Figure 7.13(1))

Figure 7.13(1)

Figure 7.13(2)

Then stretch your knees, push your hips out, protrude your abdomen, and bend your upper body backward. In the meantime, hold your hollow fists with your hands, and raise them along the sides of your body to the sides of your chest respectively. Look up in the front. (See Figure 7.13(2))

Movement 4

Shift your weight onto your right leg, while still bending your both knees. Then slowly raise your left leg up while lifting both fists above your shoulders. (See Figure 7.14(1))

Step forward with your left foot, place your left heel touching the ground, while bending your right knee to form the 'left empty-stance.' At the same time, bend your upper body forward, and release the fists into the 'tiger paw,' then pounce them forward and downward, in a circular motion, until they rest on the sides of your both knees. Palms down. Look down in the front. (See Figure 7.14(2))

Figure 7.14(1) Figure 7.14(2)

Finally lift your upper body up, and move your left foot back forming the 'standing upright with the feet shoulder width apart.'

Naturally hang your hands down beside your body. Look straight ahead. (See Figure 7.14(3))

Figure 7.14(3)

Step left (right) foot forward, and place the left heel touching the ground, with the toes up and slightly bending the left knee; meanwhile, bend the right (left) knee and squat down. Let the whole right foot rooted into the ground, with moving the right toes out about 45 degrees. Remember, keep the spine straight and the right (left)hip also should be straight line with the right (left) heel. Basically, place 70% weight on the back leg, and 30% weight on the front leg.

Movement 5

Connect the previous movement, hold the hollow fists with your hands and raise them up along the sides of your body until they rest close to your shoulders. (See Figure 7.15(1)(2)(3))

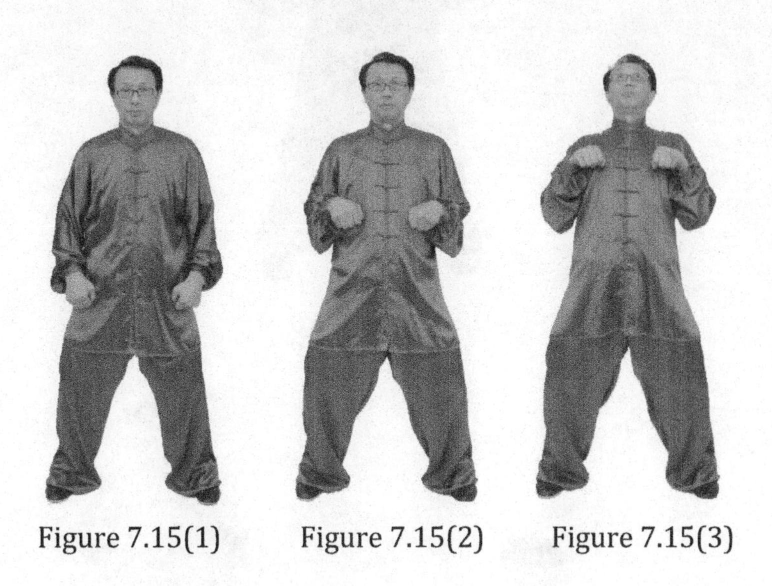

Figure 7.15(1) Figure 7.15(2) Figure 7.15(3)

Movement 6

Continue the previous movement.

Circle your hands upward and forward from your shoulders, bending your fingers to form the 'tiger paw.' Palms down. Meanwhile, bend your upper body forward, stretching your chest and settling your waist. Look straight ahead. (See Figure 7.16)

Movement 7

Bend your knees and squat down, while tucking your abdomen in and hollowing your chest. Simultaneously circle both 'tiger paws' downward toward the sides of the knees. Palms down. Look down in the front. (See Figure 7.17(1))

Figure 7.16

Figure 7.17(1) Figure 7.17(2)

Then stretch your knees, push your hips out, protrude your abdomen, and bend your upper body backward. In the meantime, hold your hollow fists with your hands, and raise them along the sides of your body to the sides of your chest respectively. Look up in the front. (See Figure 7.17(2))

Movement 8

Shift your weight onto your left leg, while still bending your both knees. Then slowly raise your right leg up while lifting both fists above your shoulders. (See Figure 7.18(1))

Figure 7.18(1) Figure 7.18(2))

Step forward with your right foot, place your right heel touching the ground, while bending your left knee to form the 'right empty-stance.' At the same time, bend your upper body forward, and release the fists into the 'tiger paw,' then pounce them forward and downward, in a circular motion, until they rest on the sides of your both knees. Palms down. Look down in the front. (See Figure 7.18(2))

Finally lift your upper body up, and move your right foot back forming the 'standing upright with the feet shoulder width apart.' Naturally hang your hands down beside your body. Look straight ahead. (See Figure 7.18(3))

Figure 7.18(3)

After repeating the movement from 1 to 8 about 3 times for each side, raise your both palms out from the sides of your body, at chest height, palms up. Look straight ahead. Then bend your elbows and close palms inward, then push them down in front of your abdomen. Naturally hang your arms down beside your body. Look straight ahead (See Figure 7.18(4)-(7)).

Figure 7.18(4)

Figure 7.18(5)

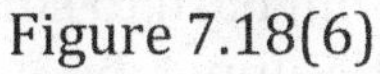

Figure 7.18(6) Figure 7.18(7)

Key points

(1) Bend the upper body forward (tiger pouncing) and extend the hands (tiger paw) out as far as possible, while pulling the hips backward to fully spread the spinal column.

(2) Bending the knees and squatting down, contracting the abdomen and hollowing the chest should be in coordination with extending the knees, pushing the hips out, protruding the abdomen, and bending the body backward. This enables the spinal column to form a creeping motion from folding to expanding.

(3) When pouncing the 'tiger paw' downward in empty stance, the practitioner should slightly run-up with the hands. First soft and then hard, with exhaling deeply and quickly. Qi should be out from the Dantian and used to push the strength. Let the internal strength reach the fingers to express the tiger's power and boldness.

(4) Senior and weak people should follow their body's condition to reduce the range of motion properly.

Intention

Focus the mind on the 'Ming-Men' acupoint while raising and pushing.

Common errors

(1) The transition between the 'tiger paw' and 'holding fists' is not mastered appropriately.

(2) The range of the motion from bending to extending is not enough. The coordination of both hands is not in harmony.

(3) When stepping forward to form empty-stance, the weight of the body does not maintain balance, causing the body to swing from left to right.

Corrections

(1) When pouncing 'tiger paws' forward, the practitioner should put the internal strength into the fingertips. The movement should be transferring from soft to hard. When circling both palms back, the 'tiger paw' should bend inward to form an empty fist. The movement should be transferring from hard to soft.

(2) When extending and protruding the upper body forward, both hands should spread backward. The route of movement should be circular so that it can help the body to complete bending and extending.

(3) When stepping forward to form an empty stance, the horizontal distance between the feet should maintain an appropriate breadth, a reasonable increase the degree of steadings.

Effect and function

(1) The movement of the 'Tiger Pouncing' makes up the extension and folding motion of the spine from front to back. Especially it leads the waist to move forward and will greatly increase the flexibility and the range of the extension of all spine joints. It also can make the spine maintain the normal physiological curvature.

(2) Spine motion can strengthen the waist muscle-power; it has a very beneficial and protective effect on some common lumbar diseases, such as lumbar muscle strain, habitual sprain disease, etc.

(3) 'Du Mai' (Govern meridian) is the lining in the middle of the back, and 'Ren Mai' (Conception meridian) is the lining in the middle of the abdomen. Extending and bending the spine forward and backward will affect the 'conception meridian' and 'govern

meridian,' and play a role in nurturing yin/yang, dredging the channel/meridian, and promoting Qi/blood circulation.

The Figures of the Continuous Movements

Tiger Play

Second Frolic: Deer Play
鹿戏

Features and life nurturing theory

The purpose of 'Deer Play' is to imitate the shape and movement of a deer, hoping to attain long life and a pure soul like a deer. The features of a deer are its gentle disposition, swift movement, fondness of pushing with horns, and running ability. When it stands, it likes stretching its neck to glance at things afar. The deer also likes looking from left to right, and at its rear foot. It is also good at moving its tail bones (sacrum). The tail bone is the place where the Ren-Mai (Conception Meridian) and Du-Mai (Governor Meridian) meet. Thus, during practicing, the practitioner not only needs to imitate the attitude of a deer with swift movement and calm spirit, but also needs to focus attention on the 'Ming-Men'. This will guide Qi to the whole body, open meridians, circulate blood, relax tendons and bones, and benefit kidneys and strengthen the lower back. It can also enhance blood circulation in the pelvic cavity.

This play is suitable for curing dysfunctional nerves in the internal organs, chronic infections of the internal organs in the abdomen, fatigue in the waist muscles, nerve pain in the pelvis, deteriorated thigh bones, osteonecrosis of the femoral head, lumbar muscle degeneration, sciatica, sexual impotence, and neurological disorders.

Deer Resisting
鹿抵

Movement 1

Connect the posture of the previous movement.

Slightly bend your knees and turn your right toes outward about 45-degree. Shift your weight onto the right leg, while lifting your left foot a little, passing through the inner side of your right foot, and then stepping forward to the left. Place your left heel touching the ground. Meanwhile, slightly turn your body to the right, hold hands both empty-fist and swing them to the right side. Both fist-hearts should face down and be at shoulder height. The eyes should follow the movement of hands. Look at your right fist. (See Figure 7.19)

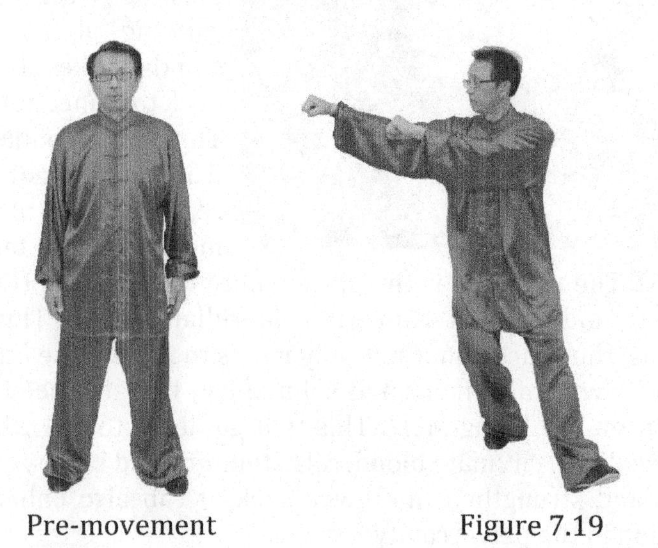

Pre-movement Figure 7.19

Movement 2

Shift your weight onto the front leg (left leg) smoothly, bend your left knee and turn your left toes outward about 45-degree rooted into the ground, while stretching right leg. Simultaneously turn your upper body to the left, release both fists into the 'deer horns,' and then bring them upward and towards the left, until they reach the other side of your body by following your body turning in a circular motion. Place both palms facing outward, fingers backward. Bend your left arm and place your left elbow tip supported by the left waist. Raise your right arm above the head, extend it to the left side and backward. Place your right palm facing outward, fingers backward. Look at the right heel. (See Figure 7.20(1)(2))

Figure 7.20(1) Figure 7.20(2)

Then turn your body to the right and bring your left foot back forming the 'stand with feet shoulder width apart.' Simultaneously release both 'deer horns' into empty- fists and bring them upward, and toward the right and drop them down in front of the hips. Look down in the front. (See Figure 7.21(1)(2)(3))

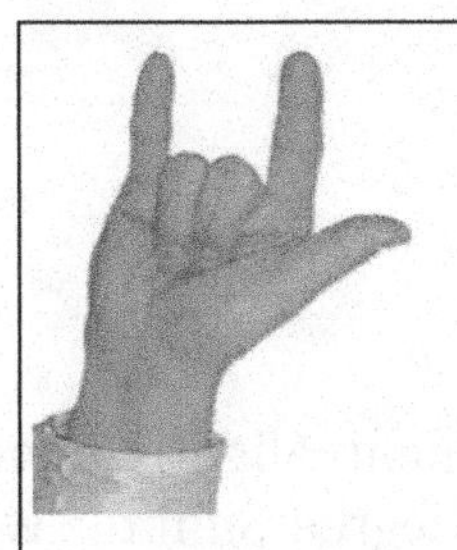

Stretch the thumb outward and extend the index and pinky up; bend the middle and ring finger inward.

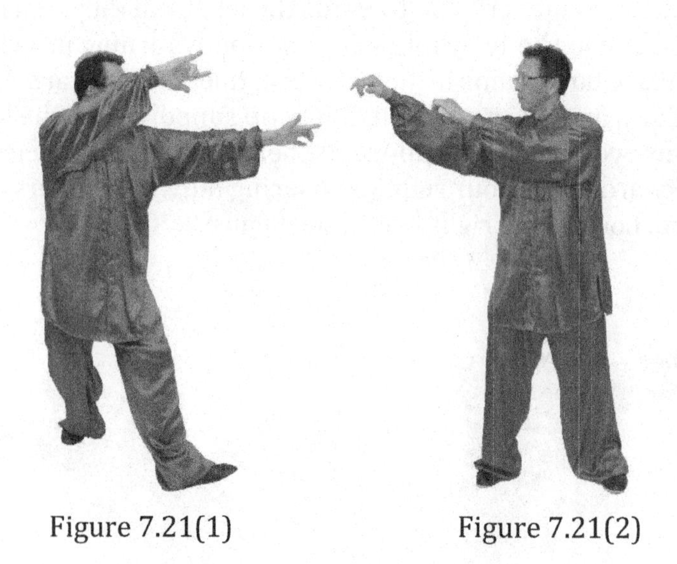

Figure 7.21(1) Figure 7.21(2)

Figure 7.21(3)

Movement 3

Connect the posture of the previous movement. Slightly bend the knees and turn the left toes outward about 45-degree. Shift the weight onto your left leg, while lifting your right foot a little, passing through the inner side of your left foot, and then stepping forward to the right. Place the right heel touching the ground. Meanwhile, slightly turn your body to the left, hold both empty-fists and swing them to the left side. Both fist-hearts should face down and be at shoulder height. The eyes should follow the movement of hands. Look at the left fist. (See Figure 7.22)

Figure 7.22

Movement 4

Shift the weight onto your front leg (right leg) smoothly, bend your right knee and turn the right toes outward about 45-degree rooted into the ground, while stretching the left leg. Simultaneously turn your upper body to the right, release your both fists into the 'deer horns,' and then bring them upward to the right, until they reach the other side of your body by following your body turning in a circular motion. Place your both palms facing outward, fingers backward. Bend your right arm and place your right elbow tip supported on the right waist. Raise your left arm above the head, extend it to the right side and backward. Place your left palm facing outward, fingers backward. Look at the left heel. (See Figure 7.23(1)(2))

Figure 7.23(1)

Figure 7.23(2)

Side

Then turn your body to the left and bring your right foot back forming the 'stand with feet shoulder width apart.' Simultaneously release your both 'deer horns' into empty- fists and bring them upward, toward the left and drop them down in front of your hips. Look down in the front. (See Figure 7.24(1)(2)(3))

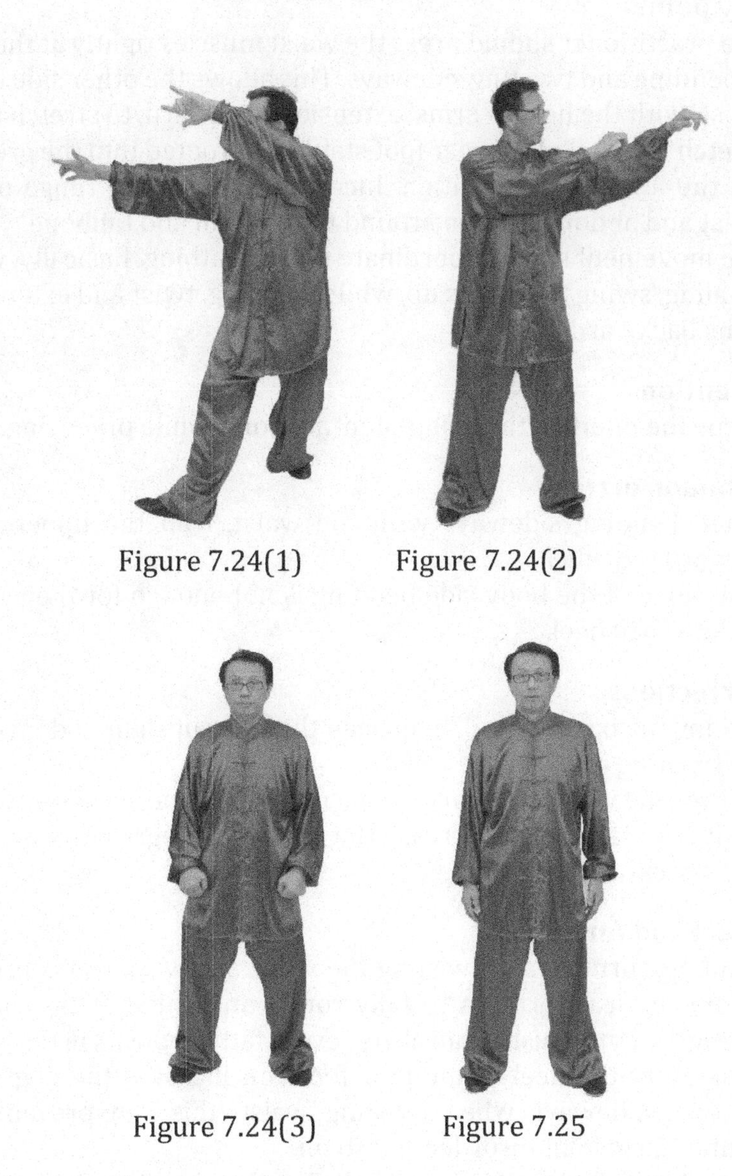

Figure 7.24(1) Figure 7.24(2)

Figure 7.24(3) Figure 7.25

Movement 5 to movement 8

Same as movement 1 to movement 4. Repeat 1 to 8 one more time. And then return to the start position. (See Figure 7.25)

Key points

(1) The practitioner should press the waist muscles tightly at the side of bending and twisting sideways. This allows the other side of the waist, with the help of arms' extension backward, to stretch fully.
(2) Stretch the heel of the rear foot stably and rooted into the ground. Fix the lower body position. Increase the twisting range of the waist and abdomen. Turn around the sacrum and tailbone.
(3) The movement should coordinate with breathing. Basically, when inhaling, swing the palms up, while exhaling, twist and extend the arms backward.

Intention

Focus the mind on the 'Ming-Men' acupoint while practicing.

Common errors

(1) When bending sideways with the waist, lean the upper body forward too much.
(2) The range of the body side bending is not enough for the eyes to see the back heel.

Corrections

(1) Sinking the back hip will help keep the body upright and increase the twisting range of the waist.
(2) Shifting the weight forward can increase the bending degree of the front knee, as well as increase the extending degree of the raised arms backwards.

Effect and functions

(1) Bending, turning, and twisting the waist sideways can cause the whole cervical vertebra to fully rotate and enhance the muscle strength of the waist. It can also prevent fatty deposits in the waist.
(2) Looking at the heel of the rear foot can increase the degree of bending sideways when twisting waist, this can prevent the lumber facet joint disorder and so on.
(3) Traditional Chinese Medicine believes that, 'lumbar is the house of the kidney'. Revolving the tailbone and sacrum can strengthen the lower back and tonify the kidney as well as strengthen the muscles and bones.

Deer Running
鹿奔

Movement 1

Connect the posture of the previous movement. Step forward with your left foot, forming the left 'bow-stance.' Meanwhile, hold your empty fists with your hands and raise them upward and forward, in a circular motion in front of the body. Now, you should slightly press your wrists downward, but still stretch your arms forward. Place arms at shoulder height and shoulder width apart. Fist-hearts down. Look straight ahead. (See Figure 7.26(1)(2))

Movement 2

Shift your weight back onto your right leg, but still place your left foot totally touching the ground while stretching your left knee and bending your right knee. Now, consciously lower your head, arch your back and tuck your abdomen in. At the same time rotate your both arms inward and extend your palms forward. Backs of your both hands should oppose each other. Release your both fists into the 'deer horns.' Look down. (See Figure 7.27)

Figure 7.26(1)

Figure 7.26(2)

Figure 7.27

Figure 7.27 side

Movement 3

Follow the previous movement. Shift your weight forward onto your left leg while lifting your upper body up and stretching your right leg to form the left 'bow-stance.' Sink shoulders and drop elbows. Rotate your both arms outward and release your both 'deer horns' into the empty-fists. Place the arms at shoulder height. Fist-hearts down. Look straight ahead. (See Figure 7.28)

Figure 7.28 side Figure 7.29

Step left (left)foot forward, so that the both heels are at one and half shoulder-width apart. Keep the right (left) leg straight but not totally extended. Bend the left (right) knee about 45 degrees and let the front leg forming vertical state.

Movement 4

Move your left foot back to form the 'stand with feet shoulder width apart.' Release your fists into the palms and drop down beside your thighs. Look straight ahead. (See Figure 7.29)

Movement 5

Step forward with your right foot, forming the right 'bow-stance.' Meanwhile, hold your empty fists with your hands and raise them upward and forward, in a circular motion, in front of your body. Now, you should slightly press your wrists downward, but still stretch your arms forward. Place arms at shoulder height and shoulder width apart. Fist-hearts down. Look straight ahead. (See Figure 7.30)

Movement 6

Shift your weight back onto your left leg, but still place your right foot totally touching the ground while stretching your right knee and bending your left knee. Now, consciously lower your head, arch your back and tuck your abdomen in. At the same time rotate your both arms inward and extend the palms forward. Back of your both hands should oppose. Release both fists into the 'deer horns.' Look down. (See Figure 7.31)

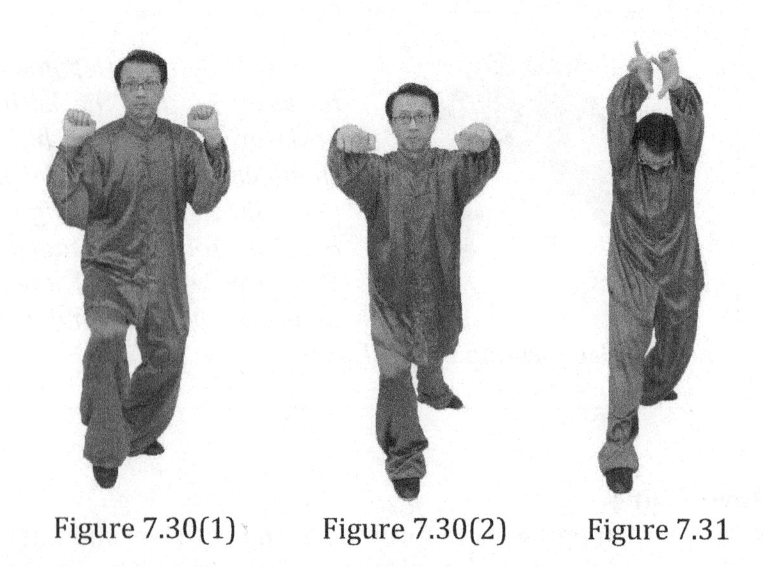

Figure 7.30(1) Figure 7.30(2) Figure 7.31

Movement 7

Follow the previous movement. Shift your weight forward onto your right leg while lifting your upper body up and stretching your left leg to form the right 'bow-stance.' Sink shoulders and drop elbows. Rotate your both arms outward and release your both 'deer horns' into empty-fist. Place your arms at shoulder height. Fist-hearts down. Look straight ahead. (See Figure 7.32)

Movement 8

Move your right foot back to form the 'stand with feet shoulder width apart.' Release your fists into the palms and drop down beside your thighs. Look straight ahead. (Figure 7.33)

After repeating the movement from 1 to 8 about 3 times for each side, raise your both palms out from the sides of your body, at chest height, palms up. Look straight ahead. Then bend your elbows and close palms inward, then push them down in front of your abdomen. Naturally hang your arms down beside your body. Look straight ahead. (Figure 7.34(1) - (4))

Figure 7.32

Figure 7.33

Figure 7.34(1)

Figure 7.34(2)

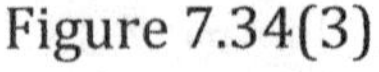

Figure 7.34(3) Figure 7.34(4)

Key points

(1) Lifting leg and stepping forward should have a circular motion; dropping the foot down needs to be gentle and swift, so that it will embody the deer's elegant and graceful manner.

(2) When shifting the weight onto the back leg, the forearms should extend forward, with hollowing the chest in as far as possible. Place the upper back forming the shape of a 'horizontal-bow.' Extend the head forward; arch the upper back backward; contract the abdomen; and tuck hips inward to form the shape of a 'vertical-bow' to make the waist and back extend and pull longer fully.

(3) The movement should coordinate with the breathing. Basically, inhale when sitting back, and exhale while shifting the weight forward.

Intention

Focus the mind on your 'Ming-Men' acupoint while practicing.

Common errors

(1) After dropping the foot down, place both feet standing on a straight line, causing the weight to be unstable, and upper body to be tense and slanting.
(2) The range of the 'horizontal-bow' of the back and 'vertical-bow' of the trunk are not obvious, too small.

Corrections

(1) After lifting the foot, step forward at the same side in front of the shoulder, Maintain the transverse space width (horizontal breadth) between the feet.
(2) Increasing the range of revolving inward of the shoulders will magnify the degree of the contracting chest. The movement of extending head and hips forward, contracting abdomen and moving back, will increase the degree of bending back of the trunk.

Effect and functions

(1) Rotating the arms inward and extending them forward can stretch the muscles of the shoulders and back. This has a preventive effect on neck-shoulder syndrome, shoulder arthritis and other diseases. Arching the back and tucking the abdomen in can correct spinal deformity, strengthen the waist and back muscle strength.
(2) When stepping forward, sink Qi to Dantian with the mind; when shifting weight backward, mobilize Qi to 'Ming-Men' to increase the exchange between innate Qi and postnatal Qi. Especially when shifting weight backward, when the whole spine is bending backward, it will greatly help to tuck the sacrum and tail-bone in, throw the 'Ming-Men' out and open the 'Da-Zhui' (Big spine) to dredge the Qi of the Du-Mai. This has the effect of uplifting the Yang Qi of the whole body.

The Figures of the Continuous ovements

Deer Play

Third Frolic: Bear Play
熊戏

Features and life nurturing theory

The purpose of 'Bear Play' is to imitate the shape and movement of a bear, which has a clumsy body, but huge power. It seems very calm outside but contains action inside. The features of the bear are its perseverance, bravery, and unwillingness to concede defeat. Although it looks clumsy and heavy, it has enormous power.

The requirement of practicing 'Bear Play' is to focus attention on the lower Dan-Tian to regulate 'Blood and Qi.' The practitioners need to show not only the heaviness and stableness of a bear, but also the lightness and quickness of a bear. Through action (*Yang*) inside and calm (*Yin*) outside, you will be able to make the brain empty and tranquil. The mind will combine with the Qi, and True Qi will penetrate into the whole body. This will effectively strengthen the spleen and benefit the stomach. The movements in this play are slow, thus it is suitable for the elderly or weaker people. It can cure many chronic diseases.

Bear Moving
熊运

Movement 1

Connect the posture of the previous movement. (See Figure 7.34(4)) Stay still for a while and regulate your breathing. Then grasp your empty fists with your hands, form the 'bear palms,' and hold them in front of your lower abdomen. Place fist-eyes opposite each other. Look down in the front. (Figure 7.35)

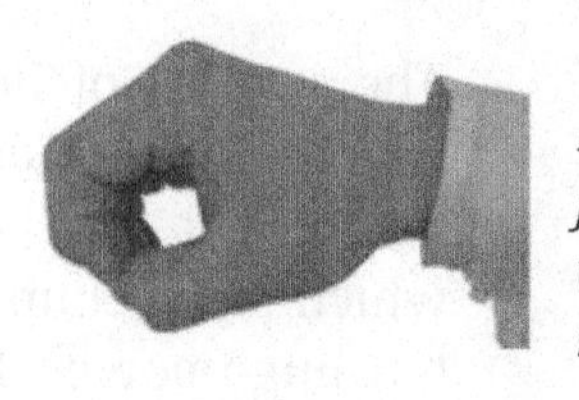

Bend all five fingers into a fist. Press thumb on the tip of the index finger. The other four fingers stick together and bend. Expand and round the tiger-mouth.

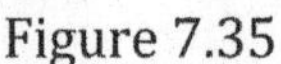

Figure 7.35 Figure 7.36(1) Figure 7.36(2)

Movement 2 (Clockwise)

Use your waist and abdomen as an axle and let your upper body swing clockwise around your lower Dan-Tian. Simultaneously draw a circle with your fists from your right rib, upper abdomen, and left rib to your lower abdomen in a circular motion. The eyes should look around with the upper body swinging. (Figure 7.36 (1) – (5))

Figure 7.36(3) Figure 7.36(4) Figure 7.36(5)

Movement 3. 4
Same as the movement 1,2. Follow the clockwise swinging about 2-4 circles and then switch the direction (counterclockwise).

Movement 5 – 8 (Counterclockwise)
Use your waist and abdomen as an axle and let your upper body swing counterclockwise around your lower Dan-Tian. Simultaneously draw a circle with your fists from your left rib, upper abdomen, and right rib to your lower abdomen in circular motion.
The eyes should look around with your upper body swinging. (See Figure 7.37 (1) - (6))

Follow the counterclockwise swinging about 2-4 circles. After completing the last movement, change your fists into palms and then drop them down beside your body naturally. Look straight ahead. (See Figure 7.38)

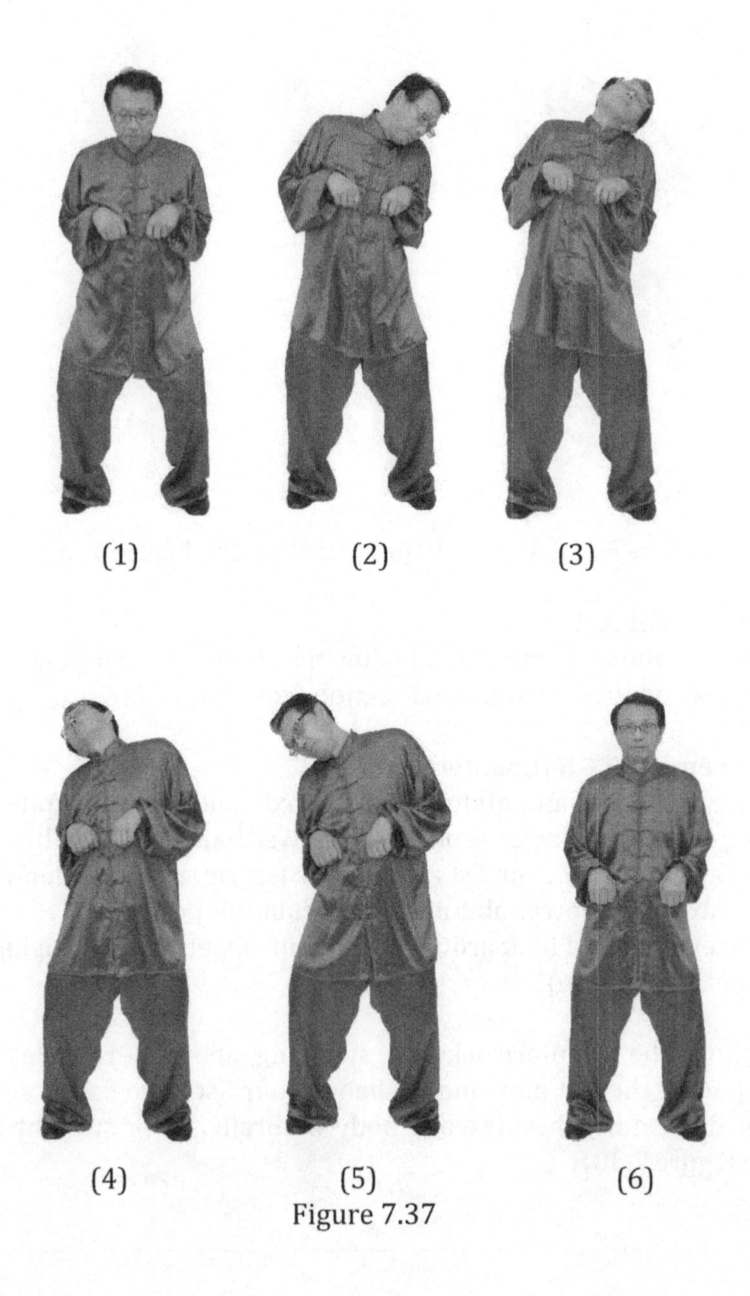

Figure 7.37

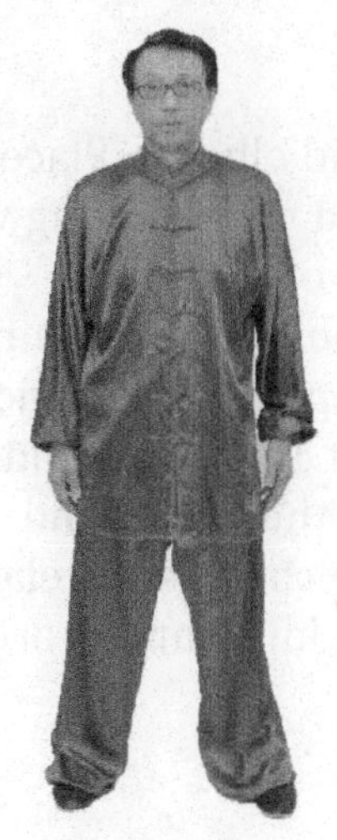

Figure 7.38

Key points

(1) Drawing a circle with the palms should follow the swinging of the waist and abdomen passively. It should be coordinated and relaxed.

(2) Drawing a circle with the palms guides Qi outside to harmonize in the physical body, while swinging the waist and abdomen leads Qi inside to nurture the internal organs. Use the mind to mobilize the 'inner Qi' (true Qi) to flow freely in the Dantian.

(3) The movement should coordinate with the breathing. Basically, inhale while raising the body, and exhale while leaning the body forward.

Intention

Focus the mind on the 'Dan-Tian' while practicing.

Common errors

(1) Pressing the abdomen too tightly with the palms or using the palms to massage the abdomen actively.

(2) The turning movement does not follow the waist and abdomen swinging naturally.

Correction

(1) Relax the shoulders and elbows. Place the palms on the waist or abdomen lightly to lead the swinging with the waist or abdomen to drive the movement of the palms.
(2) Fix the waist and hip position. As your body is swinging, imagine that you are just swinging in a vertical circle. Therefore, when swinging upward, rest the chest and contract the abdomen in order to fully extend the waist and abdomen; when swinging downward, hollow the chest, and relax the abdomen to squeeze the inner organs of 'middle-burner' areas in spleen, stomach, and liver.

Effect and function

(1) Exercising the waist joints and muscles can prevent lumbar muscle strain and soft tissue injury.
(2) Flexing the waist and abdomen, drawing the circle, and guiding the inner Qi movement can strengthen the activating functions of the spleen and stomach.
(3) Swinging the waist and abdomen can massage the digestive organs to prevent indigestion, poor appetite, abdominal distension, constipation, diarrhea and other diseases.

Bear Swaying
熊晃

Movement 1

Connect the posture of the previous movement.

Slowly and gently shift your weight onto your right leg while raising your left hip a little to lead your left foot off the floor, slightly bend your left knee. At the same time change your palms into the empty-fists like the 'bear paw' beside your body. Palms face backward. Look at the left front (See Figure7.39(1)(2)(3)).

Figure7.39(1)

Figure7.39(2)

Figure7.39(3)

Movement 2

Step to the left-front with your left foot and shift your weight to the left leg and forming the left bow-stance. Place your left toes straight forward and slightly stretch your right leg. Slightly lean your upper body forward. Hollow your chest and lift your upper back up. Keep both feet pressed flat into the floor. Meanwhile, turn your body to the right. Move your left shoulder forward while rotating your left arm in. Swing your left fist above your left knee. Place your left fist-heart facing outward. In doing so, while turning the right, naturally swing your right arm behind your right hip. Place your right fist-heart facing backward. Look forward on the left. (See Figure 7.40)

Figure 7.40

Movement 3

Turn your body to the left and shift your weight onto your right leg, slightly bending your right knee, and stretching your left leg forming a position similar to empty stance. At the same time, twist your waist and sway the shoulders to drive your arms swaying both front and back in a circular motion.

Actually, the practitioner sways the right fist from the back to the above of the left knee, with the fist-heart facing right while swaying the left fist from the front to the back of the body, with fist-heart facing back. Look at the left front. (Figure7.41)

Figure 7.41 Figure 7.42

Movement 4

Turn your body to the right and shift your weight onto your left leg again, bending your left knee, and stretch your right leg forming a stance similar to left bow-stance. At the same time, drive your left shoulder forward, rotating your left arm in while swinging your left arm above your left knee. Place your left fist-heart facing outward. In doing so, while turning the right, naturally swing your right arm behind your right hip. Place your right fist-heart facing backward. Look forward to the left. (Figure 7.42)

Movement 5

Completely shift your weight onto your left leg while raising your right hip a little to lead your right foot off the floor, slightly bending your right knee. Meanwhile, slightly turn your body to the right, while holding the 'bear paws' beside your body. Palms face backward. Look forward to the right. (See Figure7.43(1)(2)(3))

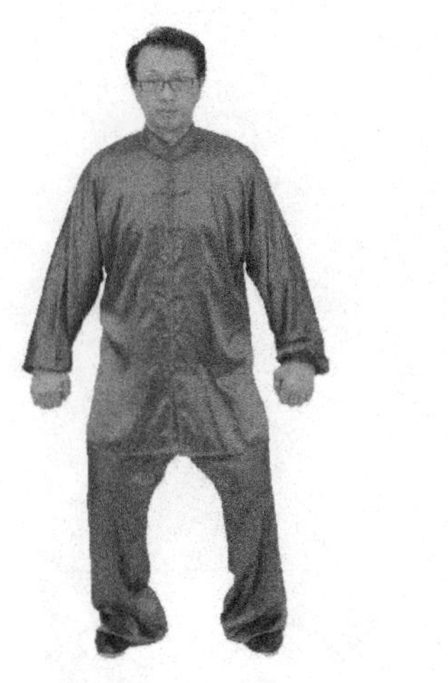

Figure7.43(1)

Figure7.43(2)

Figure7.43(3)

Movement 6

Shift your weight onto your left leg and drop your right foot forward to the right, forming the right bow-stance. Place your right toes straight forward and slightly stretch your left leg. Slightly lean your upper body forward. Keep your both feet pressed flat into the floor. Meanwhile, turn your body to the left. Move your right shoulder forward while rotating your right arm in. Swing your right fist above your right knee. Place your right fist-heart facing outward. In doing so, while turning the left, naturally swing your left arm behind your left hip. Place your left fist-heart facing backward. Look forward on the right. (See Figure 7.44)

Figure 7.44 Figure 7.45

Movement 7

Turn your upper body to the right and shift your weight onto your left leg, slightly bending your left knee, and stretching your right leg forming like an empty stance. At the same time, twist your waist and sway the shoulders to drive your arms swaying both front and back in circular motion. Actually, the practitioner sways the left fist from back to above the right knee, with fist-heart facing left while swaying the right fist from the front to the back of the body, with fist-heart facing back. Look at the right front. (See Figure 7.45)

Movement 8

Turn your body to the left and shift your weight onto your right leg again, bending your right knee, and stretch your left leg forming a stance similar to right bow-stance. At the same time, drive your right shoulder forward while rotating your right arm in and swinging your right arm above your right knee. Place your right fist-heart facing outward. In doing so, with turning the left, naturally swing your left arm behind your left hip. Place your left fist-heart facing backward. Look forward to the right. (See Figure 7.46)

Figure 7.46 Figure 7.47

After repeating the movement from 1 to 8 about 3 times for each side, step forward with your left foot to form the 'stand with the feet shoulder width apart.' Meanwhile, naturally hang your arms down beside your body. Raise both palms out from the sides of your body, at chest height, palms up. Look straight a6ead. (See Figure 7.47)

Then bend the elbows and close palms inward and push them down in front of the abdomen.

Naturally hang your hands down beside your body. Look straight ahead. (See Figure 7.48(1) – (3))

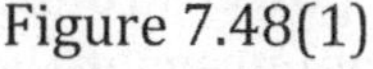

Figure 7.48(1) Figure 7.48(2) Figure 7.48(3)

Key points

(1) Use the lumbar muscle group contraction to lift the thighs, the order of the movement should be raising the hips first and then lifting the legs and bending the knees.

(2) Going forward with the feet, the horizontal distance should be slightly wider than the shoulder. The weight of the body should be shifting forward with the whole foot rooted into the ground. So, make the vibration transfer into the thigh joint. It expresses the stability and heaviness of the bear step.

Common errors

(1) Not lifting the hip while going forward, but directly bending the knee and lifting the leg.

(2) When dropping the foot forward, with powerful stomping, there is no feeling of vibration in hip joints.

Intention

Focus the mind on the 'Bobbling Spring' acupoint while practicing.

Corrections

(1) First of all, practice raising the hips on left and right. The method

is to maintain the shoulders level, shift the weight onto the right foot while lifting the left hip to bring the left leg up, then return to the original position; then shift the weight onto the left foot, while lifting the right hip, thereby experiencing the contracting state of the waist muscle groups.

(2) Raising the hip, bending the knee, shifting the weight forward, dropping the foot down naturally and placing the weight onto the whole foot. You should also relax the ankles, and knees, let the feeling of vibration transmit to the hips.

Effect and function

(1) Swinging the body from left to right, focus intention at both ribs in order to regulate the spleen and liver.

(2) Moving forward with lifting the hip, and dropping down with stomping the foot, can strengthen muscle power around the hip joints, and improve balancing ability to help prevent the elderly lower limb weakness, hip injury, knee pain and other symptoms.

The Figures of the Continuous Movements

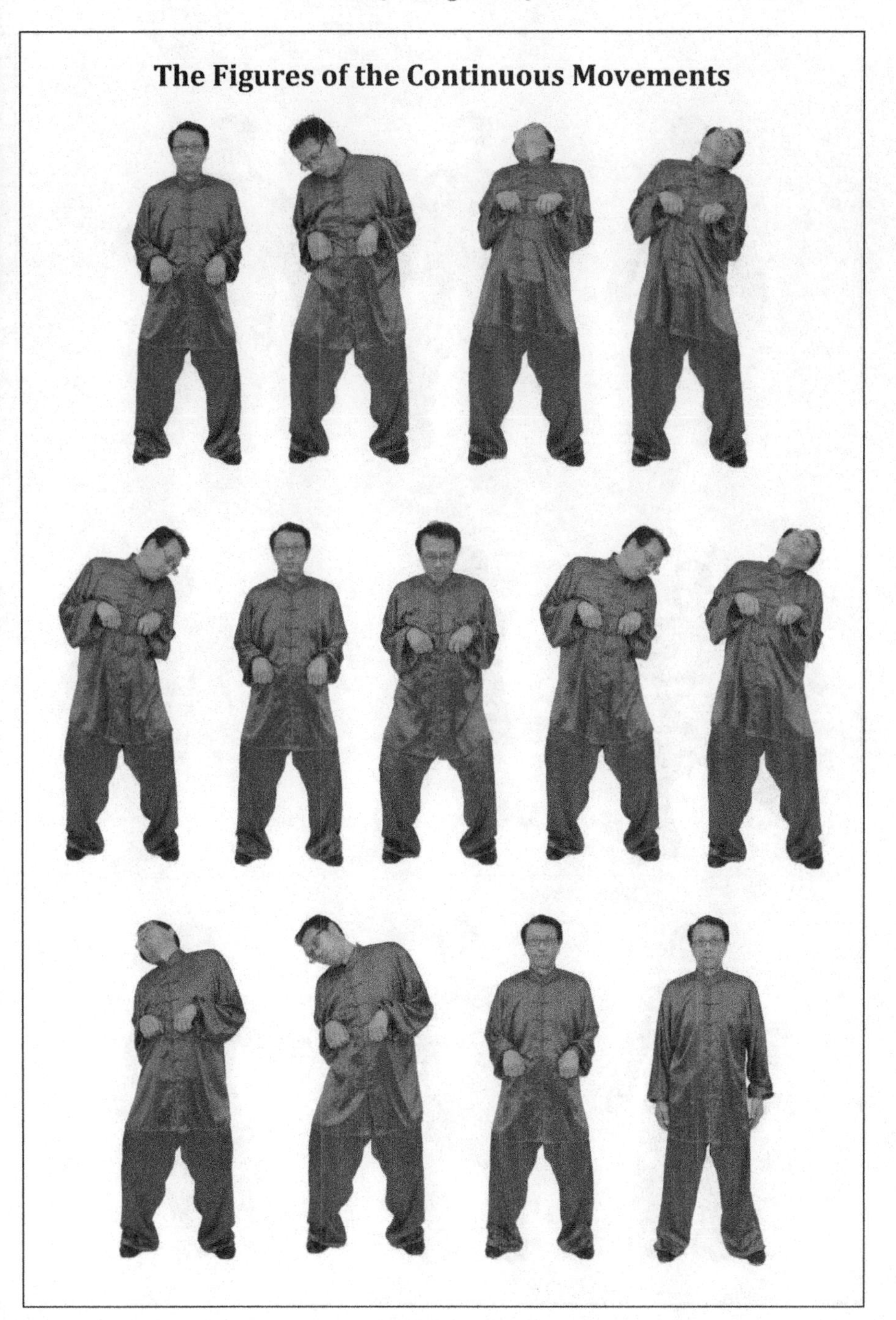

Bear Play

Great Eternal Chi

Fourth Frolic: Monkey Play
猴戏

Features and life nurturing theory

The purpose of 'Monkey Play' is to imitate the shape and movements of a monkey to show its alertness, agility, and constant motion. The features of a monkey are its ability imitate, agile movements, ability to pick fruit using upper limbs, and escaping the attacks from other animals. During practice, you need to focus your attention on the 'Lower Dan-Tian' to reach a state that 'body is moving but mind is calm.' That means you should not only practice the agility of your limbs on the outside, but also practice controlling your thoughts on the inside. The goal of 'Monkey Play' is to reach a level of 'pure and tranquil in thoughts, light but strong body,' and 'body is moving but mind is calm.' This play will enhance the functions of the heart and lungs and strengthen the kidneys and waist. This play is suitable for the older, the weaker, and depressed people. It can cure many chronic diseases.

- **Monkey Lifting 猴提**

Movement 1

Connect from the previous movement. Place your palms in front of your body, while extending your fingers and separating them naturally. (See Figure 7.49(1)) Then bend your wrists downward and combine your fingers to form the 'monkey-hook.' (See Figure 7.49(2))

Pinch the five fingers together at the tips. Bend the wrist downward.

Movement 2

Raise the 'monkey-hook' up to chest height while shrugging your shoulders, tuck abdomen in and contract the anus. At the same time lift your heels up and turn your head to the left. The eyes should follow the head moving to look at the left side. (See Figure 7.50)

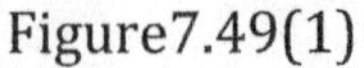

Figure7.49(1) Figure7.49(2) Figure7.50

Movement 3

Return your head to the front, sinking your shoulders, relaxing your abdomen and anus, dropping your heels down. Meanwhile release the 'monkey-hook' into the palms. Palms face downward. Look straight ahead. (See Figure7.51)

Figure 7.51

Movement 4

Press your palms down along the center of your body to the sides of your thighs. Look straight ahead (Figure 7.52(1)(2))

Figure 7.52(1)

Figure 7.52(2)

Movement 5

Connect from the previous movement.

Place your palms in front of your body, while extending your fingers and separating them naturally. (See Figure 7.53(1))

Then bend your wrists downward and combine your fingers to form the 'monkey-hook.' (See Figure 7.53(2))

Figure 7.53(1)

Figure 7.53(2)

Figure7.54

Movement 6

Raise the 'monkey-hook' up to chest height while shrugging your shoulders, tuck abdomen in and contract the anus. At the same time lift your heels up and turn your head to the right.

The eyes should follow the head moving to look at the right side. (See Figure 7.54)

Movement 7

Return your head to the front, sinking your shoulders, relaxing your abdomen and anus, dropping your heels down. Meanwhile release the 'monkey-hook' into the palms. Palms face downward. Look straight ahead. (See Figure7.55)

Figure 7.55

Movement 8

Press your palms down along the center of your body to the sides of your thighs. Look straight ahead (Figure 7.56(1)(2))

Figure 7.56(1)

Figure 7.56(2)

Repeat the movement from 1 to 8 about 3 times each side.

Key points

(1) Slightly make the 'Monkey-hook' faster when bringing the fingers together.

(2) The order of the body should be to shrug the shoulders first, then contract the abdomen, lift the anus, raise the heels and finally turn the head while raising the body's center of gravity. Shrugging the shoulders, contracting the chest, bending the elbows and lifting the wrist, all of these should be adequate.

(3) The movement could be in coordination with contracting the anus and breathing. When raising the 'monkey-hooks' up, inhale and contract the sphincter with the mind; while dropping the palms down, exhale and relax the sphincter.

Intention

Focus the mind on the 'Middle Dan-Tian.'

Common errors

(1) Balance is not maintained, after raising the heels from the ground, as a result, the whole-body shakes from front to back.

(2) No shrugging of the shoulders, or it is not enough to sufficiently handle up the chest, back and upper limbs.

Corrections

(1) Suspend the head to the top using the mind, so it will keep the whole body upright, as a result the body will be steady and balanced.
(2) Use the sternum as a center when shrinking the neck, pressing the elbows, curling the chest and contracting the abdomen. It will enhance the huddle level from the chest, back and upper limbs.

Effect and function

(1) Rapid change of the 'monkey-hook' will enhance the sensitivity of the nerve muscle reaction.
(2) When raising the 'hooks' up, the movement of shrinking the neck, pressing the elbows, curling the chest and contracting the abdomen, will strengthen breathing, massage the heart and improve brain blood supply.
(3) Lifting the heels can strengthen leg power and increase the balance of the body.

Monkey Plucking
猴摘

Movement 1

Connect from the previous movement. Step backward to the left with your left foot, place your left toes touching the ground, while bending your right knee and putting the weight onto your right leg. At the same time, bend your left elbow and change your left palm into the 'monkey-hook' and bring it to the left side of your waist. In doing so, bring your right palm forward to the right at waist height naturally. Palm down. Look at your right hand. (See Figure 7.57)

Movement 2

Shift your weight backward onto your left leg and plant your left foot into the ground solidly while bending your left knee. Draw your right foot to the inner side of your left foot, with the tiptoes touching the ground to form the 'right T-stance.' At the same time, bring your right palm down passing through your right knee, to the front of your abdomen and then place it up to the left of your head, in a circular motion. The palm should face your left temple.

The eyes should follow the right hand while your hand moves first, and then turn your head to the right to look at the right direction. (See Figure 7.58(1)(2))

Figure 7.57

Figure 7.58(1)

Figure 7.58(2)

Movement 3

Rotate your right palm inward and then press it down along the left side of your body toward the left hip. Look at the right hand.

After that, turn your body to the right, and take a big step forward to the right with your right foot, while stretching your left leg out and shifting your weight forward to your right leg. Extend your right leg, and place your left toes touching the ground. Meanwhile draw your right hand to the right-upward from the side of your left hip passing through the front of your body, in a circular motion. The drawing route of your right hand is just like a horizontal 'S' (∽).

When it is raised to the right-upward, change your hand into the 'monkey-hook,' and bring it to your right backward, in a circular motion at shoulder height or a little higher than your shoulder. In doing so, release your left 'monkey-hook' into the palm, and bring it downward, and pass through the left side to the upward, and right upward.

Then combine the five fingers to form the left 'monkey-hook' with your left wrist downward, as if 'picking the fruit.' Look at the left palm. (See Figure 7.59(1)(2))

Figure 7.59(1) Figure 7.59(2)

Movement 4

Continue the previous movement.

Shift your weight backward onto your left leg, while changing your left 'monkey-hook' into the 'wo-gu' (baby-fist) and your right 'monkey-hook' into the palm. Then drop your right palm down in front of your body naturally. The tiger-mouth faces forward. After that bend your left knee and squat down, while drawing your right foot back to close the inner side of your left foot. Place your right toes touching the ground to form the 'right T-stance.' At the same time, bend your left elbow and bring your left hand passing through your chest to the left side of your ear, in a circular motion. Place your left palm facing upward, and separate the fingers, as if 'holding a peach' in it. In doing so, draw your right palm passing through the front of your body, in a circular motion towards and under your left elbow, as if holding your left elbow up. Look at your left palm. (See Figure 7.60(1)(2))

Figure 7.60(1)

Figure 7.60(2)

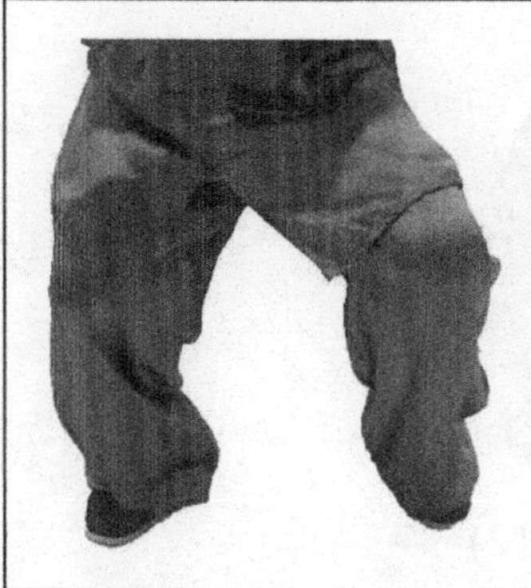

Separate the feet about 4-7 inches, with bending the knees and slightly squatting down. Then shift the weight on the right (left)leg, so that the right (left)thigh is diagonal. Raise the left (right) heel but the toes still touch the ground.

Movement 5-8

Same as movement 1 -4, only in opposite direction. (See Figure7.61, 7.62(1)(2), 7.63(1)(2),7.64(1)(2))

Figure 7.61 Figure 7.62(1)

Figure 7.62(2)

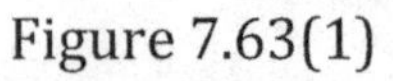

Figure 7.63(1) Figure 7.63(2)

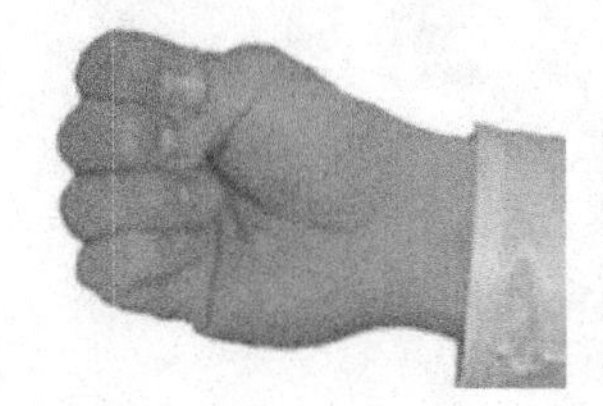

Use the tip of the thumb pinching the base of the ring finger; bend other fingers into a fist. This is for Chinese Taoism cultivation in life nurturing.

Figure 7.64(1) Figure 7.64(2)

Repeat the movement from 1 to 8 two more times. Then step your left foot to the left to form the 'stand with the feet shoulder width apart.' Meanwhile, naturally hang your arms down beside your body. (See Figure 7.65)

Figure 7.65

Raise your both palms out from the sides of your body, at chest height, palms up. Look straight ahead. Then bend your elbows and close palms inward and push them down in front of your abdomen. Naturally hang your hands down beside your body. Look straight ahead. (Figure 7.66(1)(2)(3)(4))

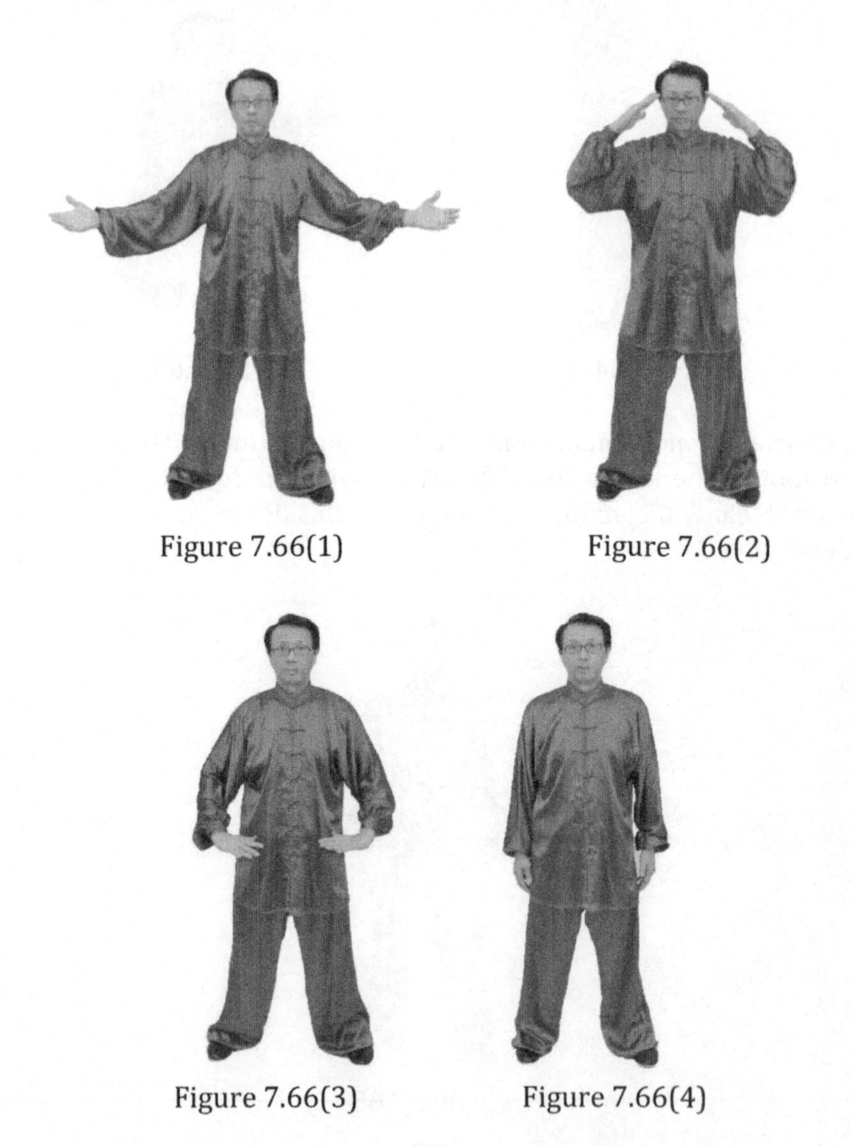

Figure 7.66(1) Figure 7.66(2)

Figure 7.66(3) Figure 7.66(4)

Key points

(1) Eyes should look around following the change of the upper limbs action in order to express the quick and agile movement of the monkey's eyes.

(2) When squatting down, the whole body should form a contractive state. When stretching the leg and stepping out, and picking fruit, the upper body and limbs should be spread out sufficiently. When picking up, the process of changing into the monkey-hook should be quick and agile. After changing the monkey-hook into the wo-gu (baby-fist), and forming the state of holding the peach, the fingers should be promptly separated.

(3) The actions are required to be alike in spirit. Pay attention to the artistic conception, but do not be overstated.

Intention

Focus the mind on the 'Middle Dan-Tian.'

Common errors

(1) The cooperation of the upper limbs and lower limbs don't coordinate with each other.

(2) When 'picking fruit,' both arms push out straightly, and without forming a circle. Not correctly timing the changing of the monkey-hook, either by not mastering it, or not catching the timing correctly.

Corrections

(1) When squatting down, bend the elbow, and put the upper arm close to the body. When stretching the leg, extend the arm out sufficiently.

(2) When 'picking fruit,' the moving route of the hand should be going upward in a circular motion. When the movement of 'picking fruit' is almost done, the palm is immediately released into the monkey-hook.

Effect and function

(1) Looking right and left will benefit for the neck action and promote blood circulation in the brain.

(2) A variety of the movements reflect the coordination between the nervous system and body movement; imitation of the ape in picking peach in a cheerful mood can relieve the tension of the brain and nervous system. It has effect on preventing nervous tension, depression and other symptoms.

The Figures of the Continuous Movements

Monkey Play

Fifth Frolic: Bird Play
鸟戏

Features and life nurturing theory

'Bird Play' is also called 'Crane Play.' It imitates the shape of a crane to show its light, smooth, and relaxed movements. The crane is a bird that is agile, has a long life, and is good at flying. The feature of a crane is its competence, yet with a light, peaceful, and free and easy attitude. It loves to turn its head to look around and has a very strong ability to balance its weight. When practicing 'Bird Play', both your arms need to imitate the flying movement, and your attention should focus on 'Qi-Hai' (sea of the Qi), which is an important acupoint in the Ren-Mai (Conception Meridian). It can generate Qi. Thus, this play can circulate Qi and blood to the whole body; unclog meridians, and exercise sinews, bones, and joints. This will increase the Qi and blood supply to the head, adjust the functions of the blood vessels in heart and bran, enhance the functions of heart and lungs, and strengthen the waist and kidneys. This play is suitable for people with high blood pressure, coronary heart disease, or shoulder infections, etc.

Bird Stretching
鸟伸

Movement 1

Connect from the previous movement.

Slightly bend your knees and squat down while folding your palms in front of your abdomen (one on top of the other, either hand up).

Point all fingers forward with palms facing down. Look at the hands. (Figure 7.67(1)(2))

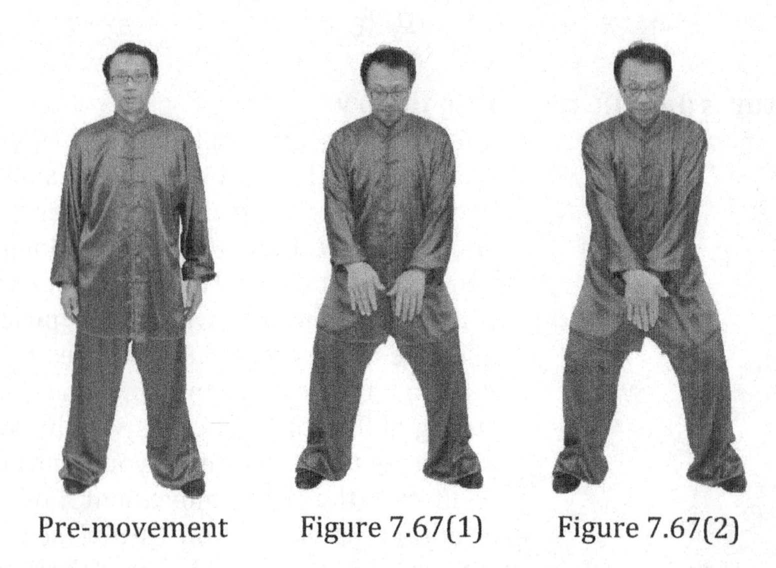

Pre-movement Figure 7.67(1) Figure 7.67(2)

Movement 2

Stretch your legs and raise your hands up to the front of your forehead, while maintaining your palms downward, and fingers forward. Slightly lean your upper body forward, shoulders upward, and neck inward; throw out your chest and drop your waist. Look down in the front. The whole movement is like a bird stretching its body before flying. (See Figure 7.68 (1)(2))

Movement 3

Slightly bend your knees and squat down while pressing your palms down in front of your abdomen. Look at the palms. (See Figure 7.69) When squatting and pressing the palms down, the lower back should be sunk, just like putting the 'Ming-Men' (between the kidneys) out and permeate Qi in it.

Figure 7.68(1) Figure 7.68(2)

Figure 7.69

Movement 4

Shift your weight onto your right leg and stretch it while lifting and extending your left leg up and backward. At the same time release your palms into the 'bird wings' and then separate them to the sides until they are behind your body. Palms backward. Now you should slightly raise your head, stretch your neck, protrude your chest and drop your waist. Look straight ahead. (Figure 7.70(1)(2))

Figure 7.70(1) Figure 7.70(2)

Spread and straighten all five fingers. Extend the thumb, index, and pinky upward. Stick the ring, and middle fingers together to downward.

Movement 5

After stretching your body, stay still for a while, and then drop your left foot to original position, bending your knees and squatting down while folding your palms in front of your abdomen (still one on top of the other, either hand up). Point all fingers forward, and palms down. Look at the hands. (See Figure 7.71)

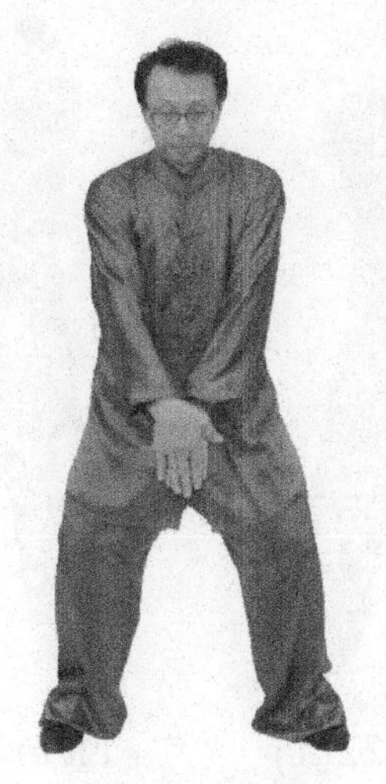

Figure 7.71

Movement 6

Stretch your legs and raise your hands up to the front of your forehead, while maintaining your palms downward, and fingers forward. Slightly lean your upper body forward, shoulders upward, and neck inward; throw out your chest and drop your waist. Look down in the front.

The whole movement is like a bird stretching its body before flying. (See Figure 7.72 (1)(2))

Movement 7

Slightly bend your knees and squat down while pressing your palms down in front of your abdomen. Look at the palms. (See Figure 7.73) When squatting and pressing the palms down, the lower back should be sunk, just like putting the 'Ming-Men' (between the kidneys) out and permeate Qi in it.

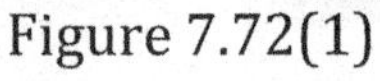

Figure 7.72(1) Figure 7.72(2)

Figure 7.73

Movement 8

Shift your weight onto your left leg and stretch it while lifting and extending your right leg up and backward. At the same time release your palms into the 'bird wings' and then separate them to the sides until they are behind your body. Palms backward. Now you should slightly raise your head, stretch your neck, protrude your chest and drop your waist. Look straight ahead. (Figure 7.74(1)(2))

Figure 7.74(1) Figure 7.74(2)

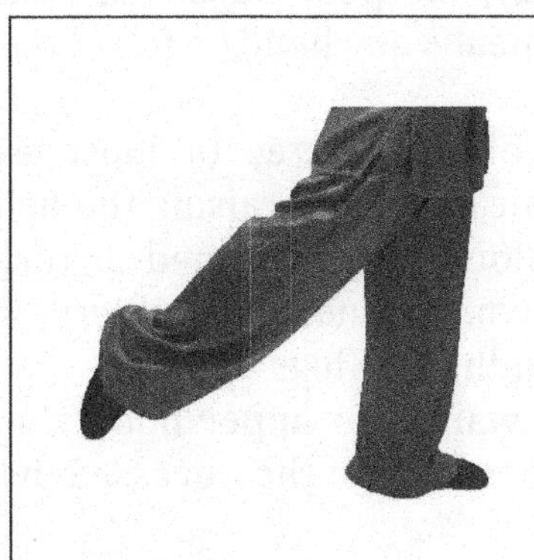

Balance with lifting one leg backward: *stand upright, using only the right (left) leg to support the body. Extend the left (right) leg and raise it backward behind the body. Stretch the tiptoes lightly and point it downward.*

Repeat the movement from 1 to 8 two more times, then drop your right foot down to form 'stand with feet shoulder width apart.'

Naturally hang your hands down to the sides of the thighs. Look straight ahead. (See Figure 7.75)

Figure 7.75

Key points

(1) Fold palms in front of the body, the position of the palms can follow whatever you like. That means one hand on top of the other, either hand is fine.

(2) Pay attention to the change of the degree of looseness and tightness of the movement. Basically, when raising the palms up, the neck, shoulders, and hip should be contracted or tucked in; while dropping the palms down, the neck, shoulders and hip should be relaxed and sunk, bending the legs slightly.

(3) When swinging the arms backward, the upper body should be stretched up in order to form the shape of the 'reverse bow.'

Intention

Focus the mind on the 'middle Dan-Tian.'

Common errors

(1) Does not master the changing of the looseness and tightness.

(2) Could not maintain balance when standing on one leg.

Corrections

(1) First practice 'folding the palms,' raise and drop them up and down in front of the body. When raising, make the hands tight, and when dropping them down, relax them. Then gradually get into the whole movement.

(2) After shifting the weight onto the supporting leg completely, lift the other leg backward. Remember, the supporting leg should be stretching out in order to improve the stability of the movement.

Effect and Function

(1) Lifting the hands up while inhaling can expand the chest and draw fresh air in; pressing the hands down while exhaling can sink Qi to Dan-Tian easily and get rid of stagnant Qi. It can enhance the 'exhale the old and inhale the new' function of the lung; increase the pulmonary capacity; improve the symptoms of chronic bronchitis, and emphysema and other diseases.

(2) Lifting the hands up can act on the 'Da-Zhui' (large spine) acupoint and the 'Wei-Lv' (tail bone and sacrum); the 'Du-Mai' will be affected; by swinging the palms backward, and making the body into reverse arcuate, the 'Ren-Mei' will be stretched. Practicing this method by alternating relaxation and tension, can enhance unclog Qi flow freely in the Governor meridian and Conception meridian.

Bird Flying
鸟飞

Movement 1

Connect from the previous movement.

Hold the palms like 'bird wings' in front of your abdomen while slightly bending your knees and squatting down. Palms diagonally face each other. Look down in the front. (See Figure 7.76)

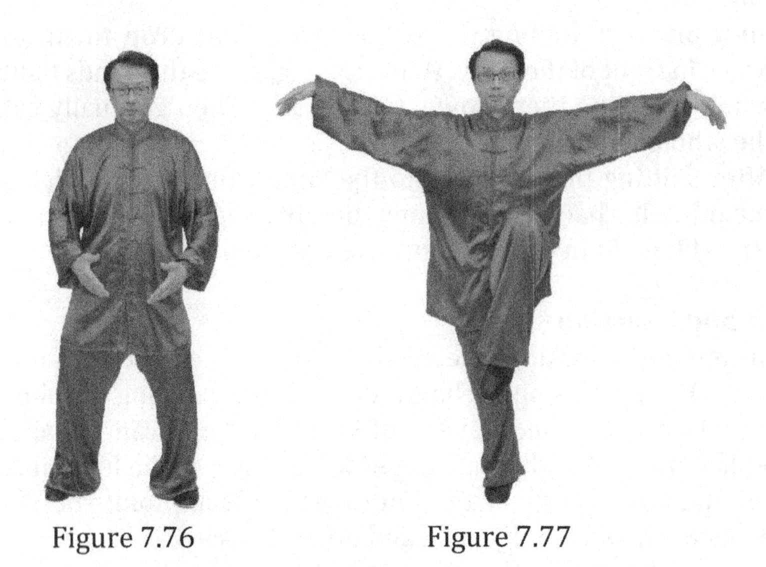

Figure 7.76 Figure 7.77

Stretch your right leg and stand it up while raising your left leg to the front, bending your left knee.

Naturally drop the left calf down with toes pointing downward. Meanwhile raise your both 'bird wings' upward to the sides of your body at the shoulders level or slightly higher than your shoulders. Palms should face downward and inward. Look straight ahead. (See Figure7. 77)

Movement 2

Drop your left foot at the inner side of your right foot, with tiptoes touching the ground (if you feel your supporting leg is strong, you do not need to drop the left foot down to touch the ground, instead you can place the left foot close to the inner side of your right ankle). Bend your knees slightly. At the same time, bring your palms downward, passing through both sides, in a circular motion and then hold your palms in front of your abdomen. Palms should diagonally face each other. Look down in the front. (See Figure7.78(1)(2))

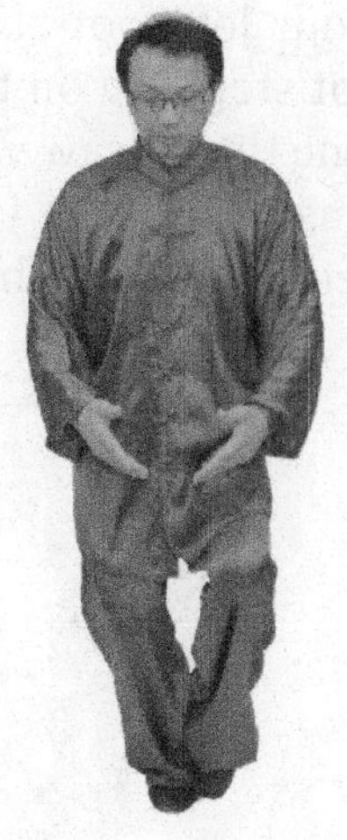
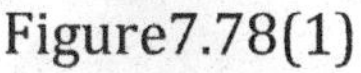

Figure7.78(1) Figure7.78(2)

Movement 3

Stretch your right leg and stand up while raising your left leg to the front and bending your left knee. Naturally drop your left calf down with tiptoes pointing downward. Meanwhile, raise your both 'bird wings' upward from the sides of your body to above your head. Make the back of your hands face each other with fingers up. Look straight ahead. (See Figure 7.79)

Balance with one knee raised (Stand on one leg): stand upright with right (left)leg. Raise the left (right) knee in front of the body and drop the lower leg and toes down naturally.

Movement 4

Drop your left foot at the inner side of your right foot, with your whole foot stepping on the ground solidly. Bend your knees slightly. At the same time, draw your arms down, in a circular motion and hold your palms in front of your abdomen. Palms should diagonally face each other. Look down in the front. (See Figure7.80)

Figure7.79 Figure7.80

Movement 5

Connect from the previous movement. Stretch your left leg and stand it up while raising your right leg to the front, bending your right knee. Naturally drop your right calf down with toes pointing downward. Meanwhile raise your both 'bird wings' upward to the sides of your body at the shoulders level or slightly higher than your shoulders. Palms should face downward. Look straight ahead. (See Figure7.81)

Figure 7.81

Movement 6

Drop your right foot at the inner side of your left foot, with tiptoes touching the ground (if you feel your supporting leg is strong, you do not need to drop the right foot down to touch the ground, instead you can place the right foot close to the inner side of your left ankle). Bend your knees slightly. At the same time, bring your palms downward, passing through both sides, in a circular motion and then hold your palms in front of your abdomen. Palms should diagonally face each other. Look down in the front. (See Figure7.82(1)(2))

Movement 7

Stretch your left leg and stand up while raising your right leg to the front and bending your right knee. Naturally drop your right calf down with tiptoes pointing downward. Meanwhile, raise your both 'bird wings' upward from the sides of your body to above your head. Make the back of your hands face each other with fingers up. Look straight ahead. (See Figure7.83)

Figure7.82(1)

Figure7.82(2)

Figure 7.83

Figure7.84

Movement 8

Drop your right foot at the inner side of your left foot, with your whole foot stepping on the ground solidly. Bend your knees slightly. At the same time, draw your arms down, in a circular motion and hold your palms in front of your abdomen.

Palms should diagonally face each other. Look down in the front. (See Figure7.84)

After repeating the movement from 1 to 8 about 3 times for each side, maintain the position of the 'standing with the feet shoulder width apart.' Meanwhile, raise both palms out from the sides of your body, at chest height, palms up. Look straight ahead.

Then bend your elbows and close palms inward and push down in front of your abdomen. Naturally hang your arms down beside your body. Look straight ahead. (Figure 7.85(1) – (4))

Figure 7.85(1)

Figure 7.85(2)

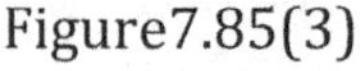
Figure7.85(3) Figure7.85(4)

Key points

(1) When raising the arms up from the sides of the body, the action should be extended, and the range of the movement should be big. Try to outspread the sides of the chest. When dropping the arms down and holding them inward, squeeze and press the sides of the chest as much as you can tolerate.

(2) The actions of the four limbs should be coordinated and smooth. The whole movement (raising and dropping) should be synchronous practicing.

(3) The movement could be in coordination with breathing. Basically, inhale when raising the arms up, exhale when dropping them down.

Intention

Focus the mind on the 'middle Dantian.'

Common errors

(1) Swinging of the arms is straight and stiff while raising and dropping them.

(2) The body is too tense, and that causes the standing to be unsteady, and the breathing uneven.

Corrections

(1) When raising the arms up, the strength should be released from the shoulders. Sink the shoulders first, and then relax the elbows, finally raise the wrists. This is the movement of the peristaltic process. When dropping arms down, relax the shoulders first, and then sink the elbows, finally press the palms down and hold them in front of the abdomen.

(2) When raising the arms up, inhale deeply. The head should be suspended up to the top. Pull in the chest and tuck the abdomen in. When dropping the arms down, relax the waist and abdomen and sink the Qi to Dan-Tian with the mind.

Effect and Function

(1) Moving the arms up to down, can change the volume of the thoracic cavity. If the movement is combined with respiratory motion, it can play a role in massaging the heart and lungs and enhancing blood oxygen exchange capacity.

(2) Stretching the thumbs and index fingers up can stimulate the 'Lung Meridian,' strengthen the 'Lung Qi' circulation and improve cardiopulmonary function.

(3) Standing on one leg can improve the body's balancing ability.

The Figures of the Continuous Movements

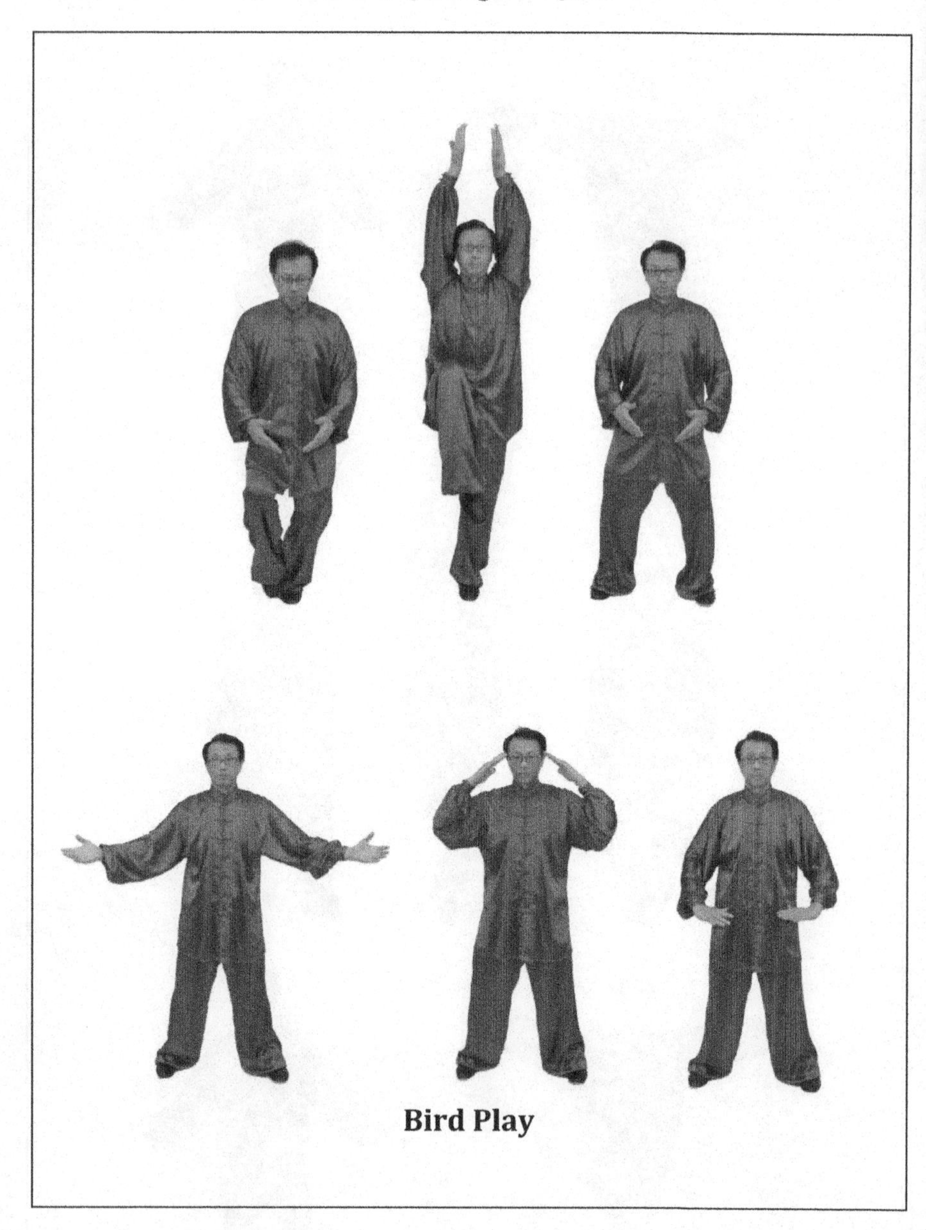

Bird Play

Concluding Form
Guide Qi Returning to the Dan-Tian
引气归元

Movement 1

Raise your palms above your head from the sides of your body. Palms face downward, diagonally. (See Figure 7.86)

Figure7.86

Figure7.87

Movement 2

Point your fingers opposing each other and slowly press palms down along the center of your chest to the front of your abdomen. Look straight ahead. (See Figure 7.87)

Repeat the movement 1 and 2 two times.

Movement 3

Drawing your horizontal circle out with your palms in front of your body slowly. Place your palms opposing each other, at the navel height. Look straight ahead. (See Figure 7.88)

Movement 4

Fold your both palms in front of your abdomen covering the Dan-Tian, crossing the 'tiger-mouth.' Basically, place your left palm inside for male and right palm inside for female. Slightly close your eyes or drop your eyelids down for nurturing Qi. Now regulate the breathing consciously and concentrate the mind on Dan-Tian. (Figure7.100)

Figure7.100

Movement 5

After a few minutes, slowly and gently open your eyes, place both palms coming together, and rub them in front of your chest until you feel them warmer. (Figure7.101)

Movement 6

Put your palms on your face, and massage it from up to down about 3 to 5 times. It is called 'dry wash the face.' (Figure7.102)

Movement 7

After washing your face, move your palms up passing through the top of your head, along the back of your ears down to your chest. Then naturally drop them down to the sides of your thighs. Look straight ahead. (Figure7.103)

Movement 8

Bring your left foot back close to your right foot, with your front sole touching the ground first, then place your whole foot onto the ground, returning the original preparation posture. Look straight ahead. (Figure7.104)

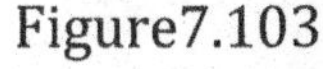

Figure7.103 Figure7.104

Key points

(1) Relax the entire body from the top of the head (Crown Point) to the sole of the feet (Bubbling Spring acupuncture point) while pushing palms downward.

(2) When drawing the horizontal-circle with the palms in front of the abdomen, the movement of the connection should be ease and smooth, like you are drawing Qi in and embracing it returning to Dan-Tian.

Intention

Focus the mine on 'Lower Dan-Tian'

Common errors

(1) Lifting the shoulders and chest up while raising the palms.
(2) The route of the palms' movement is not clear.

Corrections

(1) Make the weight of the body stable. When raising palms up, pay attention to sinking and relaxing the shoulders.
(2) Focus the mind or intention on the palms when raising palms up from the sides of the body or drawing the horizontal circle in front of the abdomen.

Effects and Function

(1) The purpose of 'Leading the Qi returning to the Dan-Tian,' is to make the Qi and breathing gradually smooth and gentle. Guide the internal Qi to Dan-Tian. It harmonizes Qi and blood, cleans the meridians and regulates the internal organs.
(2) The purpose of rubbing the hands and massaging the face, is to return to regular state, and complete the practice.

The Figures of the Continuous Movements

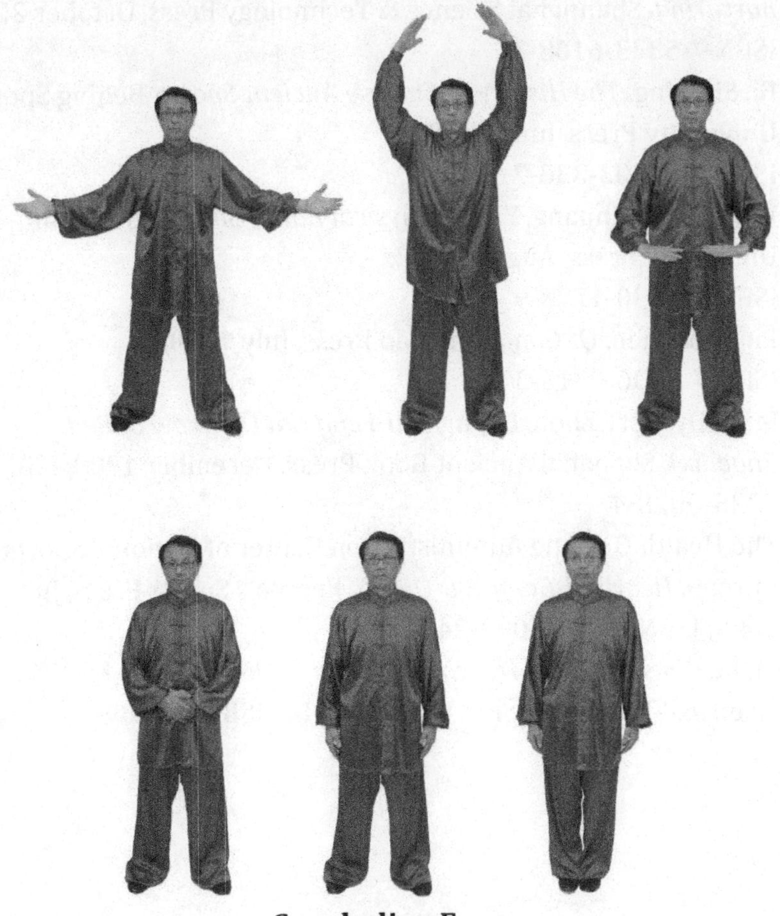

Concluding Form
Guide Qi Returning to the Dan-Tian

References:

1. Yu, DingHuai, *Traditional Chinese healthcare sports & life-nurturing,* Shannghai Science & Technology Press, October 2001, ISBN 7-5323-6168-3
2. Bi, ShiMing, *The History of Chinese Ancient Sports,* Beijing Sports University Press, June 1990, ISBN 7-81003-338-7
3. Wang, Hao, Zhuang, YaJun, *Physical Education Study,* Hehai University Press, August 2002, ISBN 7-5630-1773-9
4. Lin, Houshen, *Qi-Gong,* Qingdao Press, July 1980, ISBN 7-5436-0715-3
5. Ming Dynasty Zhou, Lujing, *Chi-Feng-Sui (Morrow of Red Phoenix),* Shanghai Ancient Book Press, December 1989, ISBN 7-5325-0028-4
6. The Health Qi-Gong Administration Center of National Sports Bureau, *Heath Qi-Gong Wu-Qin-Xi,* People's Sports Press, July 2003, ISBN 978-7-5009-2431-9
7. Yi, Ke, *Illustration of Internal & external Qi-Gong*, Nei Men Gu Science &Technology Press, April, 1988, ISBN 7-5380-1

About the Author

Yajun Zhuang, elected at eight years old among thousands of children in a talent search for Professional Wushu (Martial Arts) team in Jiangsu Province, China, has immersed his life into Chinese Martial Arts since then. At his earlier age, he was perfused with Professional Martial Arts training and spontaneously cultured with the inner spirit of Martial Arts. He initiated his own coaching career by organizing his own Wushu Team at 16 years old. At 17, he deepened his knowledge of Wushu culture and philosophy at Nanjing Normal University.

After graduation from university, Yajun Zhuang has achieved significant professional reputations, including the youngest Professor at Nanjing Industrial University in China, Member of Chinese Physical Education Committee, Board member of Wushu Professional Committee, and Senior National Wushu Judge. He has served as Chief-Judge in various national and international Wushu tournaments.

As a Wushu Scholar, Yajun Zhuang has published over twenty papers and five books in both Chinese and English. Based on his outstanding contributions to Wushu, he was enlisted in1990 Who's Who: Chinese Wushu and in 'China Wushu Encyclopedia'. Further, he was named as 'Honorary Consultant' for Chinese Wushu Hall of Fame.

In 2003, Yajun Zhuang turned his life path from China to America and broadened his passion in the West. In 2005 he joined Department of Kinesiology at Louisiana State University (LSU), teaching Chinese Martial Arts and researching how Tai-Chi and Qi-Gong affect patients with peripheral neuropathy and Parkinson's disease. His modified Zhuang's Tai-Chi Qi-Gong Therapy has demonstrated great benefits for improving patient's functional mobility and life quality. This promising and successful program has been widely reported through television, newspaper, and magazines and has had a huge influence on the community.

In 2011, Yajun Zhuang had founded 'Zhuang's Tai-Chi & Kung-Fu Academy' in Baton Rouge, Louisiana. Since then he has coached dozens of students, and they have won multiple medals and grand champions in Wushu competitions in America, including various styles of Tai-Chi, Kung-Fu, Ba-Gua, and Xing-Yi.

Like an ancient hermit, Yajun Zhuang never pauses a moment to pursue his life mission, to be an essential Chinese Wushu practitioner and propagator. He refreshes himself with different senses constantly when he teaches the same routine of Qi-Gong, Tai-Chi. That is the reason why he needs to spend years to complete the manuscripts of 'The Principle of Qi-Gong Life Nurturing,' 'Wu-Qin-Xi,' 'Ba-Duan-Jin,' ''Yi-Jin-Jing' and 'Tai-Chi-Chuan' notation.

As in Chinses Tao culture, nobody is able to tell you what Tao is, you need a mentor to guide you to approach it. Based on his longtime of cultivating, Yajun Zhuang is the mentor to guide you approach the essence of Chinese Wushu.